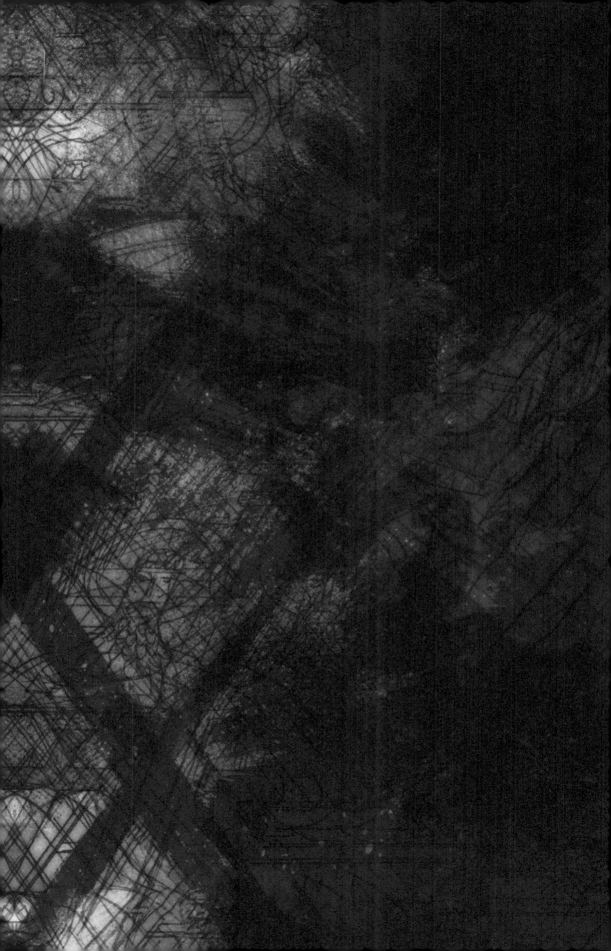

BATMAN CURSE OF THE WHITE KNIGHT

BATMAN
CURSE OF THE WHITE KNIGHT

SEAN MURPHY Writer and Art
KLAUS JANSON Artist for *Von Free*
MATT HOLLINGSWORTH Color
ANDWORLD DESIGN Letter
SEAN MURPHY and MATT HOLLINGSWORT
Cover Art and Original Series Cove
BATMAN created by BOB KANE with BILL FINGE

MARK DOYLE Executive Editor, DC Black Label and Editor – Original Series
MAGGIE HOWELL Associate Editor – Original Series
EB WOODARD Group Editor – Collected Editions
COTT NYBAKKEN Editor – Collected Edition
TEVE COOK Design Director – Books
OUIS PRANDI Publication Design
UZANNAH ROWNTREE Publication Production

OB HARRAS Senior VP – Editor-in-Chief, DC Comics

IM LEE Publisher & Chief Creative Officer
OBBIE CHASE VP – Global Publishing Initiatives & Digital Strategy
ON FALLETTI VP – Manufacturing Operations & Workflow Management
AWRENCE GANEM VP – Talent Services
LISON GILL Senior VP – Manufacturing & Operations
ANK KANALZ Senior VP – Publishing Strategy & Support Services
AN MIRON VP – Publishing Operations
ICK J. NAPOLITANO VP – Manufacturing Administration & Design
ANCY SPEARS VP – Sales
ONAH WEILAND VP – Marketing & Creative Services
ICHELE R. WELLS VP & Executive Editor, Young Reader

C Comics, 2900 West Alameda Ave., Burbank, CA 91505
rinted by Transcontinental Interglobe, Beauceville, QC, Canada. 8/7/20.
irst Printing.
BN: 978-1-77950-448-7
arnes & Noble Exclusive Edition ISBN: 978-1-77950-968-0

brary of Congress Cataloging-in-Publication Data is available.

PEFC Certified
This product is
from sustainably
managed forests and
controlled sources
PEFC
PEFC/01-31-106   www.pefc.org

"If he was the good guy, what does that make me?"

DON'T FORCE MY HAND, GENERAL--*SURRENDER.* LEAVE THIS VALLEY AND GIVE ME WHAT'S MINE.

ARE YOU REALLY SO WILLING TO PAY THE PRICE?

AKK!

WHAT PRICE?

GOTHAM VALLEY IS CURSED, *LORD WAYNE.*

THERE ARE *DEMONS* IN THESE DARKENED FORESTS-- ANCIENT ONES THAT SEEP FROM THESE MOUNTAINS AND RIVERS AND FLOW THROUGH THE VILLAGE AT NIGHT.

NO ONE IS SAFE--THEY'LL TURN YOU INTO A MONSTER *LIKE THE REST OF US.*

SORRY, *LAFFY...*

...I DON'T BELIEVE IN CURSES.

ARKHAM MANOR, 1685.

ARKHAM ASYLUM, TODAY.

I SHUT OFF THE CAMERAS, BUT YOU NEED TO BE QUICK.

WE'RE ALL VERY INTERESTED IN WHAT YOU HAVE TO OFFER.

BOOP, BOOP BEEP

OF COURSE YOU ARE.

HERE'S THE BAG YOU ASKED FOR. AND THE KEYS TO YOUR OLD CELL--

YOU'RE COMING WITH ME.

BUT--WHAT IF SOMEONE SEES ME?

YOU AND YOUR FRIENDS WANT WHAT I HAVE? THEN WE DO IT MY WAY. LIKE ALWAYS.

Bruce,

I know you waited for as long as possible before reading this. Because you're too frightened to let me go, and because you don't know how to say good-bye.

No doubt my death made you feel more alone than ever, causing you to retreat into that dark place where you think no one can find you. And you probably tried to push everyone away, convinced that only the isolation would give you the strength to return. But you were wrong. And that's always been hard for you to understand.

That there's no strength in being alone.

I'm happy you're finally reading this, because it means you now understand. It means Barbara and Richard are there with you, as I doubt you could have read this without them. It means you understand how their love is essential to moving forward.

But most importantly, it means you're ready to say good-bye. Good-bye, my son.

Alfred

P.S.: Check the loose floorboard in my quarters. There's something there you're ready to see.

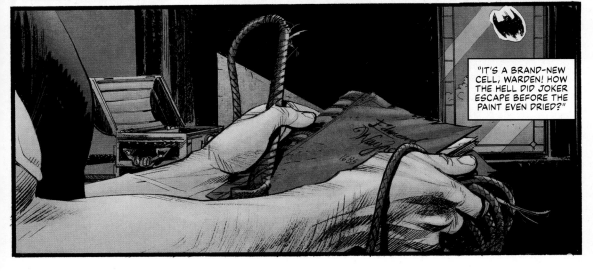

"IT'S A BRAND-NEW CELL, WARDEN! HOW THE HELL DID JOKER ESCAPE BEFORE THE PAINT EVEN DRIED?"

JOKER DOESN'T USUALLY MISS. YOU'RE A LUCKY MAN.

YEAH? I DON'T FEEL *LUCKY*.

AND YOU WERE STABBED RIGHT HERE IN THIS HALLWAY?

YES.

WRONG.

WHAT?

AN ATTACK LIKE THAT CREATES *CAST-OFF PATTERNS* AND *SPATTER* ON THE WALL.

NOT A *CLEAN PUDDLE OF BLOOD* ON THE FLOOR.

WHAT ARE YOU SAYING?

DO YOU WANT TO TELL US WHERE JOKER REALLY STABBED YOU, OR DO YOU JUST WANT US TO ARREST YOU FOR *HELPING HIM ESCAPE?*

I THINK I NEED MY--

WHERE'S THE JOKER?!

AHH...I DON'T KNOW! HE WENT TO HIS OLD CELL, THEN HE LEFT!

RIGHT
ON TIME,
RUTH.

YOU REVEALED YOURSELF TO GORDON, AND NOW YOU WANT TO TELL EVERYONE ELSE IN GOTHAM?

ARE YOU OUT OF YOUR MIND?

NAPIER WAS RIGHT--THERE ARE TOO MANY *UNINTENDED CONSEQUENCES* OF BATMAN.

WHAT ABOUT THE *UNINTENDED CONSEQUENCES* OF SUDDENLY TELLING THEM THE TRUTH?

NOT JUST FOR YOU, BUT FOR THE ENTIRE WAYNE LEGACY?

YOU COULD COMPROMISE EVERYTHING YOUR FAMILY EVER WORKED FOR!

I'M NOT MAD AT NAPIER, I'M MAD AT MYSELF--I HAD *NO EXCUSE* FOR GETTING IT WRONG!

WHAT DO YOU MEAN?

LOOK AROUND.

I HAD AN INFINITE AMOUNT OF WEALTH AND RESOURCES, AND I SPENT DECADES USING THEM TO PURSUE ONE *SINGLE GOAL*--TO MAKE GOTHAM A BETTER PLACE.

THAT'S EXACTLY WHAT GORDON SAID.

WELL HE'S RIGHT! IF YOU WANT TO LEGITIMIZE YOURSELF, THEN JOIN THE GTO. HELP US WITH THE NAPIER INITIATIVE.

I'M SORRY, DICK. I CAN'T.

YOU WON'T JOIN BECAUSE IT HAS NAPIER'S NAME ON IT, RIGHT?

WELL, THAT'S BULLSHIT--NAPIER WASN'T THE JOKER, HE WAS THE GOOD GUY!

AND IF HE WAS THE GOOD GUY, WHAT DOES THAT MAKE ME?

THAT'S NOT WHAT I--

YOU WANT ME TO ADMIT IT, FINE--NAPIER DID A LOT OF GOOD! HE EXPOSED THE CORRUPTION AND THE HYPOCRISY AND USHERED IN A NEW ERA FOR GOTHAM.

BUT HE TOOK ME DOWN IN ORDER TO DO IT!

IT WAS MY ONLY JOB, AND I FAILED!

AND THE ONLY REASON I FINALLY SAW MY MISTAKES WAS BECAUSE MY GREATEST ENEMY RUBBED MY FACE IN THEM.

THAT'S WHY I CAN'T JOIN THE GTO--BECAUSE I DON'T KNOW HOW LONG BATMAN HAS LEFT.

I MEAN, YOU'RE IN THAT HOUSE ALL ALONE NOW.

I'M NOT SAYING YOU NEED TO TALK TO ME OR DICK, BUT YOU NEED TO TALK TO *SOME-BODY.*

IF IT MAKES YOU FEEL BETTER, I'LL CALL LESLIE.

DON'T DO IT FOR ME, BRUCE. DO IT FOR YOURSELF.

CAN WE TALK ABOUT THE CASE NOW?

WHAT HAVE YOU GOT?

RESULTS CAME BACK ON THE BONES--THEY'RE OVER THREE-HUNDRED YEARS OLD.

THAT'S A LONG TIME TO BE BURIED IN ARKHAM ASYLUM.

IT WASN'T ALWAYS AN ASYLUM. IT USED TO BE *FORT ARKHAM.*

BEFORE THAT, IT WAS JUST A STONE HOUSE BELONGING TO *LAFAYETTE ARKHAM.*

LAFFY ARKHAM, THE VAMPIRE FROM THAT OLD *CHILDREN'S POEM?*

EVERY KID IN GOTHAM KNEW IT...

LAFFY ARKHAM IN THE WOOD EATING CHILDREN WHEN HE COULD...

UNDERNEATH A MOON OF BLOOD, SWEPT AWAY BEFORE THE FLOOD.

DAD USED TO RECITE THE POEM ON HALLOWEEN TO SCARE THE SHIT OUT OF ME. HE THOUGHT IT WAS HILARIOUS.

ARKHAM WAS A BRITISH GENERAL WHO CONTROLLED GOTHAM VALLEY IN THE 1600s.

AND A VAMPIRE.

THAT'S...A *REALLY* BIZARRE COINCIDENCE.

WHAT DOES IT SAY?

IT'S TOO BRITTLE TO OPEN AND READ--I'LL NEED TIME TO RESTORE IT.

THAT WASN'T THE ONLY THING IN THE CHEST. THERE WAS ALSO A WHIP...

...MADE FROM *BAT LEATHER.*

I DON'T KNOW WHAT JOKER HAS, BUT IT GOES ALL THE WAY BACK TO THE FOUNDING OF GOTHAM CITY.

AND SOMEHOW INVOLVES THE *WAYNES.*

HOW ARE YOU FEELING?

I DON'T THINK THE PRAYERS ARE HELPING, FATHER.

BAD NEWS?

GAVE ME SIX MONTHS. WITH CHEMO, MAYBE A YEAR.

JEAN-PAUL. I'M SO SORRY.

IT'S OKAY.

YOU KNOW YOU DON'T HAVE TO DO THAT.

KEEPS ME FOCUSED. I'M HERE A LOT-- MIGHT AS WELL PITCH IN.

MAYBE IT'LL SCORE ME *BONUS POINTS* WITH THE MAN UPSTAIRS.

MAYBE HE'LL LOOK PAST ALL THE HORRIBLE SHIT I'VE DONE.

YOUR FAMILY HAS A LONG HISTORY WITH US, JEAN-PAUL. YOU KNOW IF YOU EVER NEED ANYTHING--

I KNOW.

SAFE NIGHT, JEAN-PAUL.

FLICK

... FATHER, IS THAT YOU?

PUT THAT DOWN, JEAN-PAUL. YOU'RE NOT A JANITOR...

...YOU'RE A KING. THE RIGHTFUL HEIR TO GOTHAM.

THE WARS, THE SICKNESS, THE GHOSTS IN YOUR NIGHTMARES-- GOD HASN'T BEEN *TORTURING* YOU...

...HE'S BEEN *PREPARING* YOU.

THEY MURDERED YOUR ANCESTOR AND SEIZED YOUR LAND. AND FOR SEVEN GENERATIONS THEY'VE SAT ON YOUR THRONE.

...ARE... ARE YOU AN *ANGEL?*

YES. I'M HERE TO REVEAL YOUR *HOLY DESTINY...*

CLANG

...THE TRUTH BEHIND YOUR NAME, *BEHIND THE VALLEY.*

GOD NEEDS YOU, *AZRAEL...*

"It's not enough to kill Batman—we need you to *become* Batman."

JUST TELL ME ONE THING BEFORE WE SEND YEH AWAY, *THIEF.*

THAT HOUSE IS A FORTRESS. HOW'D YOU GET IN WITHOUT CALLING ATTENTION FROM THE GUARD?

AND HOW'D YOU KNOW WHERE THIS *RING* WAS HIDDEN?

I GREW UP IN THAT HOUSE.

HA! THAT HOUSE WAS BUILT BY ONE OF THE GREATEST FAMILIES IN ALL OF LONDON.

BUT EVERYONE KNOWS THEY DIED IN THE PLAGUE.

SO THAT EITHER MAKES YOU A LIAR OR A *BASTARD.*

KLINK

OR A *GHOST.*

GUARD, YOU'RE COMING AS WELL. TO GIVE TESTIMONY.

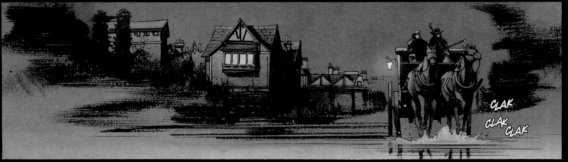

CLAK
CLAK CLAK

ARE YOU A GHOST, *EDMOND WAYNE?*

OR ARE YOU AN OUTCAST?

THE LAST OF A NOBLE BLOODLINE WHO TRIED TO FLEE HIS DESTINY?

I NEVER TOLD YOU MY FIRST NAME.

TELL ME-- DO YOU BELIEVE THAT *GOD HAS A PLAN* FOR EACH OF US?

I DON'T BELIEVE IN GOD.

WELL, I DO. AND I DON'T BELIEVE THIS WAS HIS PATH FOR YOU. I THINK YOU'RE *MEANT FOR SOMETHING GREATER.*

YOU'RE NOT A GUARD.

NO, I'M A MESSENGER. *A PRIEST.* AND I OFFER YOU A CHOICE, BUT YOU MUST DECIDE QUICKLY.

YOU CAN ACCEPT YOUR CURRENT FATE, ROTTING INSIDE THE HELL OF NEWGATE HERE IN LONDON. OR YOU CAN ACCEPT THAT GOD HAS OTHER PLANS FOR YOU...

...BY COMING WITH ME.

FINE, I ACCEPT GOD! WHATEVER GETS ME OUT OF *PRISON--*

GOOD.

KLAK

WHAT... WHAT ARE YOU GOING TO DO?

GOD'S WILL.

While they didn't die by my hand, they died for my freedom. And the guilt weighs heavily on my soul. For I've never taken a life, nor do I ever intend to.

The olive-skinned priest seems undaunted—no doubt he's taken many lives. But he claims to be driven by a higher purpose, ordained by God.

Bakkar hails from the Beqaa Valley, a place deep in the Ottoman where his family traded in wine.

I know of a long tradition of warrior-priests from that part of Persia, but the Crusades have long ended.

Bakkar claims the Templars never disappeared from the Holy Land—they just split into smaller factions. Like the Order of St. Dumas, which he serves.

Bakkar was sent to the New World to spread the word of God to the colonists.

Ever the brave warrior, he chose to settle in the place that needed him the most.

Gotham Village is a place of sin, and a haven for smugglers and pirates. Controlled by a corrupt general who stole the land from its rightful owners.

His name is Lafayette Arkham, but villagers know him as Laffy.

Supposedly he's a vampire— a demon who feeds on the blood of small children.

I don't believe in such stories. But Bakkar does.

GENERAL *Lafayette* *Arkham*

His quest is to cleanse Gotham of this demonic infestation.

TOMORROW WE BEGIN YOUR TRAINING.

All he needs is an heir of the family who has legal claim to the valley...

...someone whom the British would be forced to recognize as Gotham's rightful lord...

...someone who would force Arkham out...

...someone to end the illegal trade...

...someone brave enough to help him bring peace to the innocent people of Gotham.

WIFF

All Bakkar needs...

...is a Wayne.

Gotham Valley is all my family has left.

So this is where we make our stand.

However, Bakkar's help comes at a heavy price... half of Gotham.

This might not be something I'm willing to grant...

SOMEONE HERE TO SEE YOU, MR. WAYNE.

SHE DOESN'T HAVE AN APPOINTMENT.

IT'S IMPORTANT, MR. WAYNE. I'M HERE ABOUT YOUR *BAT PROBLEM*.

...

LET HER IN.

THIS WILL GO A LOT QUICKER IF YOU STOP PLAYING STUPID AND JUST ACCEPT THE FACT THAT RIGHT NOW, I KNOW MORE ABOUT BRUCE WAYNE THAN YOU DO.

WHO ARE YOU?

WHAT CAN I DO FOR YOU, MISS...

YOU AND THE POLICE CAN LAY OFF MY CLIENTS, MR. WAYNE. OUR MUTUAL FRIEND *THE JOKER* TOLD ME EVERYTHING.

THERE MUST BE SOME MISUNDER-STAND--

MY NAME IS *RUTH,* AND I CREATED THE BATMAN DEVASTATION FUND. I'M ALSO THE FINANCIAL HANDLER FOR SOME OF GOTHAM'S WEALTHIER CITIZENS--THE PEOPLE NAPIER CALLED *"THE ELITES."*

AND I'M HERE TO POINT OUT THAT IT'S IN *BOTH OUR INTERESTS* FOR YOU TO MAKE THE NAPIER INITIATIVE GO AWAY.

HOW ABOUT THIS INSTEAD--YOU GIVE ME A LIST OF YOUR CLIENTS, AND I WON'T *THROW YOU INTO ARKHAM*.

SECRECY IS A TOP PRIORITY IN MY LINE OF WORK. YOU'LL NEVER FIND OUT WHO MY CLIENTS ARE-- IN FACT, SOME OF THEM *DON'T EVEN KNOW* THEY'RE CLIENTS.

BESIDES, WE'RE NOT DOING ANYTHING ILLEGAL.

"...OR ANYONE ELSE YOU'VE ROPED INTO YOUR CAUSE."

YOU ALL KNOW I'M NOT A POLITICIAN.

I'M JUST A BLUE-COLLAR KID WHO WANTED TO BE AN UNDERPAID COP.

I'M NOT GOOD AT *SPIN*, I DON'T LIKE *CAMERAS*, AND I HAVE *NO PATIENCE* FOR BULLSHIT.

SO I'M GOING TO BREAK THE RULES OF POLITICS AND BE HONEST WITH YOU...

I. HATED. JACK. NAPIER.

UNLIKE THE VOTERS, I DIDN'T HAVE THE LUXURY OF IGNORING ALL THE HORRIBLE THINGS JOKER DID TO HIS VICTIMS.

AND I WAS *STUNNED* WHEN HE GOT ELECTED AS COUNCILMAN. SUDDENLY I DIDN'T RECOGNIZE THE CITY I WAS LIVING IN-- I FELT BETRAYED.

AND FOR A LONG TIME I REFUSED TO BELIEVE THAT JACK NAPIER WAS A DIFFERENT PERSON THAN THE JOKER. THAT BURIED INSIDE GOTHAM'S *WORST CRIMINAL* WAS GOTHAM'S *BEST CHANCE* AT MOVING FORWARD.

BUT I WAS WRONG.

JACK NAPIER WAS NOT THE JOKER. AND WHILE HE WASN'T PERFECT, HE *DID* SHOW US HOW TO BE BETTER. AND THAT'S WHY WE CREATED THE *NAPIER INITIATIVE.*

AS COMMISSIONER I ENDED POLICE CORRUPTION, ADDRESSED THE PROBLEMS IN PLACES LIKE BACKPORT, AND SUPPORTED PROGRAMS LIKE THE GTO. BUT THE ROOT OF THE PROBLEM ISN'T ON OUR STREETS, IT'S IN OUR *IVORY TOWERS.*

THAT'S WHY I'M ASKING FOR YOUR SUPPORT. GIVE ME THE POWER TO STOP THE SO-CALLED *ELITES.*

NOT AS YOUR COMMISSIONER, BUT *AS YOUR MAYOR!*

TSSSS

BWAHAHAHAHAHA!

...IT DOESN'T LOOK LIKE WAYNE IS GOING TO COOPERATE. SO, MR. VALLEY, *YOU'RE PLAN B.*

AZRAEL.

AZRAEL...

...YOU MIND PULLING YOUR SWORD OUT OF MY MAHOGANY DESK?

I DON'T HAVE TIME FOR YOUR SCHEMES.

FOR ME, IT'S VERY SIMPLE...BRUCE'S FAMILY TOOK MY KINGDOM IN *COLD BLOOD,* AND THAT'S *EXACTLY* HOW I'M GOING TO TAKE IT BACK.

HOW?

MICHAEL IS A SNIPER. GABRIEL IS DEMOLITIONS. OUR SPECIALTY WAS DISRUPTING ENEMY NETWORKS BY REMOVING *KEY PLAYERS.*

I LOOK AT GOTHAM, AND I SEE A LOT OF *KEY PLAYERS.*

THEN IT SOUNDS LIKE WE BOTH WANT THE SAME THING.

BLOOD.

IT'S NOT ENOUGH TO *KILL* BATMAN--WE NEED YOU TO *BECOME BATMAN.*

OUR BATMAN.

IN EXCHANGE, WE'LL MAKE YOU VERY RICH. *LIKE A KING.*

I DON'T PLAN ON SURVIVING THIS.

YOU HAVE MORE TIME THAN YOU THINK, JEAN-PAUL. WE CAN GIVE YOU CANCER TREATMENTS YOU'D NEVER BE ABLE TO AFFORD OTHERWISE.

YOU COULD LIVE A FULL LIFE.

THIS ISN'T THE *MIDDLE AGES*--YOU WANT GOTHAM BACK, THEN YOU'LL HAVE TO DO IT IN THE 21ST CENTURY. I'M YOUR BEST BET.

JUST TELL ME WHAT YOU NEED.

FORGET BEING MAYOR, AND FORGET WHAT THIS MEANS FOR ME AS COMMISSIONER...

...WHAT I'M MOST CONCERNED ABOUT IS THAT YOU DIDN'T THINK YOU COULD BE HONEST WITH ME!

I DIDN'T TELL YOU FOR YOUR OWN PROTECTION.

JOKER WAS RIGHT! I SPENT YEARS WORKING ALONGSIDE MY OWN DAUGHTER, BUT I NEVER NOTICED BECAUSE OF A SILLY LEATHER MASK.

YOU'RE A HELL OF A DETECTIVE, JIM.

AND YOU! ALL YOUR TALK OF TRUST AND TURNING OVER A NEW LEAF. YOU SAID YOU'D REVEAL YOURSELF TO GOTHAM! WHEN EXACTLY WERE YOU PLANNING ON DOING THAT?

YOU TOLD ME NOT TO. SAID THAT IT WOULD ONLY COMPLICATE THINGS.

WELL I WAS WRONG!

YOU SHOULD HAVE COME OUT, WAYNE!

THEN MAYBE JOKER AND THE ELITES WOULDN'T HAVE DESTROYED MY LITTLE GIRL'S LIFE.

YOU KEEP FORGETTING...

..I'M THE ONLY ONE IN GOTHAM YOU CAN'T SNEAK UP ON.

GRRRR

BABIES-- SHOOSH.

JOKER'S IN CUSTODY. I NEED YOUR HELP INTERROGATING HIM.

I DON'T GIVE TWO SHITS ABOUT THE JOKER, BATS. YOU KNOW THAT.

WHAT ABOUT JACK NAPIER?

...   JACK'S GONE.

YOU DON'T KNOW THAT.

I CAN'T GO DOWN THIS ROAD AGAIN. MY HEART CAN'T TAKE IT.

BESIDES, I HAVE OTHER THINGS TO WORRY ABOUT.

YOU'RE PREGNANT?!

WORLD'S GREATEST DETECTIVE.

"A LITTLE CONSPICUOUS, JP..."

WON'T HE PROTECT US BETTER IN *CAMOUFLAGE?*

THE FIRE AND THE COLORS ARE SYMBOLS OF *ST. DUMAS.* MY ANCESTORS JOINED *THE ORDER* YEARS AGO, AFTER THEY LOST CONTROL OF GOTHAM.

IT WOULD MEAN A LOT TO ME IF YOU WORE THEM.

OF COURSE, I'D BE HONORED, JP.

MICHAEL-- YOU READY?

HE'S READY.

LOAD UP THE DOLPHIN.

TIME TO BREAK SOME STARCH.

*HOLY SHIT--*RUTH REALLY CAME THROUGH WITH THIS STUFF.

COMPUTER-- MATCH 1685 MAP WITH MODERN MAP.

GOTHAM

NONCOMPATIBLE. RESERVOIR AND COAST- LINES INCONSISTENT.

THE 1685 MAP MUST BE WRONG. SHOW THE LOCATION OF GOTHAM RESERVOIR.

GOTHAM

WHAT THE HELL?

ALERT--SECURITY BREACH. RESERVE FIREWALL--

IN THE BEGINNING, GOTHAM HAD TWO SONS.

THE BROTHERS WERE TO DIVIDE THE LAND AND LIVE IN PEACE. BUT THEN ONE SON ROSE AGAINST THE OTHER, LIKE CAIN AND ABEL.

GOD CURSED CAIN FOR WHAT HE'D DONE--JUST AS HE CURSED YOU. JUST AS HE CURSED ALL OF GOTHAM.

I AM VENGEANCE. I AM GOD'S WRATH, HERE TO BREAK THE CURSE, TO RISE UP AGAINST YOU AND DELIVER THIS LAND FROM EVIL.

AFTER THREE CENTURIES, THE HOUSE OF WAYNE WILL FINALLY BE RECTIFIED.

CRASH

IRRRRT

VROOOOOO

WHUDD

‡HRRRNGH‡

FZZRT

"Just what Gotham needs—another colorful wacko."

...BUT NOT LIKE THIS.

I KNOW. BELIEVE ME, *I KNOW.*

BUT THIS IS A GOOD THING--IF WE'RE GOING TO TRACK THIS GUY DOWN, WE'LL NEED TO KNOW EVERYTHING HE AND THE JOKER KNOW.

I ONLY CAUGHT A GLIMPSE OF HIM-- STRANGE MASK, RED CLOAK, BIG SWORD.

HE USED HATTER TO *HACK INTO THE SECURITY SYSTEM,* THEN HE TURNED THE ENTIRE BATCAVE *AGAINST ME.* I WAS ABLE TO REGAIN CONTROL OF THE BATMOBILE RIGHT BEFORE HE *DETONATED THE ENTIRE MANSION.*

HOW DID HE FIND YOU?

I THINK HE WAS SENT BY A WOMAN NAMED *RUTH.*

WHO?

SHE WALKED INTO MY OFFICE AT WAYNETECH THE OTHER DAY--SAID THAT SHE WAS WORKING WITH THE JOKER, AND THAT SHE KNEW EVERYTHING ABOUT ME.

BLACKMAIL?

SOME BIG BALLS ON HER.

SHE REPRESENTED THE ELITES, AND WANTED ME TO COOPERATE BY STOPPING THE *NAPIER INITIATIVE.*

AND YOU LET HER WALK RIGHT OUT OF YOUR OFFICE?

I HAD TO--SHE KNEW ABOUT *YOU AND BARBARA.* I HAD NO WAY OF KNOWING WHAT *SOMEONE LIKE THAT* WAS CAPABLE OF.

I DON'T UNDER- STAND--IF THEY KNOW WHO YOU ARE, THEN WHY WOULD THEY BOTHER EXPOSING *ME?*

BECAUSE WITHOUT ME, THEY CAN'T MAKE MONEY ON THE BATMAN DEVASTATION FUND.

THEY NEED BATMAN...

OR A VERSION OF BATMAN WHO WILL COOPERATE WITH THEM...

...ONE WITH A RED CAPE AND A BIG SWORD.

JUST WHAT GOTHAM NEEDS, ANOTHER **COLORFUL WACKO.**

NO, IT'S DIFFERENT THIS TIME--HE'S NOT JUST ANOTHER SUPER-CRIMINAL...

...THE JOKER PICKED THIS MAN **FOR A REASON.**

THE JOURNAL AND THE MEDALLION FROM JOKER'S CELL?

IT'S THE SYMBOL OF AN ANCIENT CULT. **THE ORDER OF ST. DUMAS.** THE MAN IN THE CLOAK WAS WEARING **THE SAME THING.**

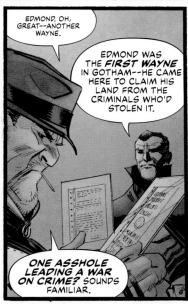

EDMOND. OH, GREAT--ANOTHER WAYNE.

EDMOND WAS THE **FIRST WAYNE** IN GOTHAM--HE CAME HERE TO CLAIM HIS LAND FROM THE CRIMINALS WHO'D STOLEN IT.

ONE ASSHOLE LEADING A WAR ON CRIME? SOUNDS FAMILIAR.

EDMOND WASN'T ALONE. HE HAD A PARTNER NAMED **BAKKAR** WHO WORE THIS SYMBOL. EDMOND WAS SUPPOSED TO GIVE BAKKAR **HALF HIS LAND** IN EXCHANGE FOR HIS HELP.

SO THE GUY WHO BLEW UP YOUR HOUSE IS A DESCENDANT OF BAKKAR?

OR JOKER **CONVINCED** HIM HE IS.

GORDON'S ON THE PHONE--HE'S READY TO **INTERROGATE** THE JOKER.

I'LL MEET YOU THERE.

BRUCE, **YOU JUST LOST YOUR HOME...**

...SHOULDN'T YOU TAKE SOME TIME OFF? SO YOU DON'T--

TURN INTO A GODDAMN PSYCHO AND GO OFF THE DEEP END **LIKE LAST YEAR.**

JOKER THINKS HE HAS **ALL THE CARDS.**

THE ONLY WAY TO THROW HIM OFF IS TO **SURPRISE** HIM.

...THE CHANCE TO HAVE A *REAL* FAMILY?

PANT PANT PANT

YOU'RE JUST TRYING TO *TRICK ME* INTO HELPING YOU GET *JACK NAPIER* BACK.

PANT PANT WHIMPER

IT'S NOT A TRICK.

LIAR.

YOU'D *KNOW* IF I WAS LYING TO YOU.

EVEN IF WE GOT HIM BACK, WHO'S TO SAY HE'LL STAY THAT WAY? I'M ABOUT TO BE A MOM. IT'S NOT JUST ABOUT *ME* ANYMORE--

I WON'T LET HIM HURT YOU, HARLEY. *I PROMISE.*

I NEED YOU TO *TRUST ME.*

...

NOW THAT WE'RE **ALONE**, LET'S GO BACK TO THE PART ABOUT WHY YOU DECIDED TO TELL ME YOU ARE REALLY A **HANDSOME BILLIONAIRE.**

JOKER ALREADY KNEW--I FIGURED YOU DID AS WELL.

SORRY, BUT I CALL BULLSHIT--I MIGHT NOT KNOW **BRUCE WAYNE**, BUT I KNOW **YOU.** AND YOU KNOW WHAT I THINK?

I THINK YOU **LIKE ME!**

I'D **LIKE** YOU TO GET YOUR HEAD EXAMINED...

COME ON--ADMIT IT! WE HAD A ROCKY START, BUT OVER THE YEARS YOU AND I HAVE BECOME **BUDDIES!**

REMEMBER THAT DRESS YOU BOUGHT ME?

THE ONE YOU WON'T LET ME FORGET ABOUT?

IT FIT PERFECTLY. WHICH MEANS YOU EVEN KNEW MY **BRA SIZE!**

I'M A DETECTIVE.

HAHA, SURE. **THAT'S IT.**

SO THIS IS WHERE YOU FOUND OL' LAFFY, HUH?

WHO DO YOU THINK KILLED HIM?

THERE WERE TWO MEN--ONE WAS A PRIEST NAMED BAKKAR.

AND THE OTHER WAS **EDMOND WAYNE.**

OOOOOH, SO THIS IS A **FAMILY MATTER.**

AND IT GOES BACK TO THE **ORIGINAL WAYNE** AND THE **ORIGINAL JOKER?**

PRETTY EPIC--I CAN SEE WHY JOKER'S **GEEKING OUT** OVER THIS.

LOOKS LIKE A COMPLETE SKELETON.

SOME TRAUMA TO THE KNEES, PROBABLY FROM WHEN HE HIT THE GROUND.

SURPRISED THEY MISSED THIS DURING LAFFY'S EXCAVATION.

AARRRGGH!

PLEASE, GOD--THIS IS *NOT HAPPENING NOW*--

CONTRACTIONS? I THOUGHT YOU SAID IT WAS A FALSE ALARM--

WELL I WAS WRONG!

COME ON, LET'S--

SHOVE THE CHUNKY BLONDE THROUGH A TINY PASSAGEWAY? *NO THANKS!*

WE'RE DOING IT HERE!

TELL ME YA GOT *BAT-STRENGTH PAINKILLERS* IN YOUR BELT!

IT'S NOT A GOOD IDEA. WE DON'T KNOW HOW SAFE--

GIMME THE DRUGS!

HARLEY, TRY TO RELAX--

NOW!

OR I SWEAR TO GOD I'LL MAKE YOU FIGHT A PREGNANT WOMAN!

BRATTATATATA

AH!

WHUD

BLAM

AARRGH!

"You and I chose this. And so did your father."

"WHAT'S THE MATTER, PUMPKIN?"

I DON'T WANT TO GO TO SCHOOL ANYMORE.

"...I THOUGHT YOU LIKED SCHOOL?"

I DO, BUT--

DID SOMEONE HURT YOU?

A BOY ON THE PLAYGROUND. I PUSHED HIM WHEN HE TRIED TO KISS ME.

"GOOD!"

BUT THEN HE PUSHED ME BACK. AND I FELL.

MY LIP WAS BLEEDING.

DID YOU TELL THE TEACHERS?

NO...

"...I DIDN'T WANT HIM TO GET INTO TROUBLE."

LISTEN TO ME--NEXT TIME SOMEONE HURTS YOU, I WANT YOU TO HURT THEM BACK. *HARDER.*

BUT...HE'S A BOY AND HE'S BIGGER THAN ME.

THAT DOESN'T MATTER.

BUT ISN'T FIGHTING AGAINST THE RULES?

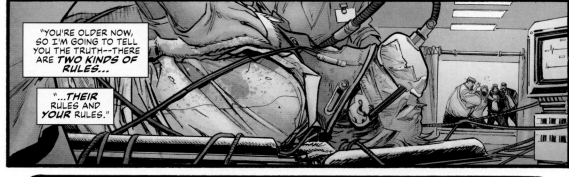

"YOU'RE OLDER NOW, SO I'M GOING TO TELL YOU THE TRUTH--THERE ARE *TWO KINDS OF RULES*...

"...*THEIR* RULES AND *YOUR* RULES."

FROM NOW ON, *YOUR RULES* SAY THAT YOU FIGHT BACK.

WON'T I GET IN TROUBLE WITH MY TEACHERS?

YOU LET ME WORRY ABOUT YOUR TEACHERS.

THANKS, DAD.

AND DON'T TELL MOM WHAT I SAID. YOU'LL ALWAYS BE HER LITTLE PRINCESS, AND SHE'D BE HEARTBROKEN IF SHE LEARNED *THE TRUTH*.

WHAT'S THAT?

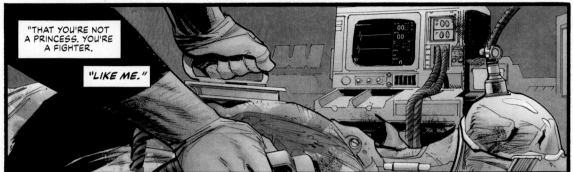

"THAT YOU'RE NOT A PRINCESS, YOU'RE A FIGHTER."

"LIKE ME."

BYE, DAD. I LOVE YOU.

GOODBYE, PUMPKIN.

ANYTHING FROM THE CRIME SCENE?

NOT YET. YOU?

COMBING THROUGH EVERY SECURITY CAMERA IN THE AREA. *BLOCK BY BLOCK.*

BABS...

DON'T.

...MONTOYA IS GOING TO ORDER YOU TO TAKE A LEAVE OF ABSENCE. SO YOU HAVE TIME TO GET OVER THE LOSS--

THEN I'LL QUIT THE GTO. NO ONE CAN STOP ME FROM FINDING HIM.

YOU KNOW I LOST MY PARENTS, TOO. *AS DID BRUCE.*

I'M JUST SAYING...YOU KNOW YOU'RE NOT ALONE. YOU'LL ALWAYS HAVE A--

THIS ISN'T A FAMILY, DICK.

YOU KNOW WHO FIRST TOLD ME THAT? *YOU.*

WELL, I SHOULDN'T HAVE SAID THAT. IT'S JUST...I SPENT A LONG TIME BEING ANGRY--

YOU *SHOULD* BE ANGRY. *WE ALL SHOULD.*

BABS--

CAPES, COWLS, AND SECRET IDENTITIES--THIS INSANITY RUINED OUR LIVES. BUT NO ONE WANTS TO SAY ANYTHING BECAUSE WE'RE IN TOO DEEP.

HE'S OUT OF HIS MIND, DICK! AND WE ALL BOUGHT INTO IT!

PULL YOUR HEAD OUT OF YOUR ASS-- THIS ISN'T WORKING!

I'M NOT IN THE HABIT OF DEFENDING HIM...

...BUT YOU'RE NOT BEING FAIR--YOU AND I CHOSE THIS.

AND SO DID YOUR FATHER.

IF YOU NEED ME, YOU KNOW WHERE TO FIND ME.

CUSTOMIZED MILITARY VEHICLE FROM THE 1970S?

THAT'S GOTTA BE HIM.

"HOW MANY SAFE HOUSES DO YOU HAVE?"

SURE THIS IS WHAT YOU WANT?

I...I FOUND THIS VEHICLE PARKED NEAR THE ATTACK. SO I RAN IT THROUGH THE SYSTEM AND GOT A MATCH FROM A HIGHWAY CAM ON THE GOTHAM INTERSTATE.

AND YOU DON'T PLAN ON ARRESTING HIM?

NO. I DON'T.

BATMAN, COME IN. BATGIRL AND BULLOCK ARE MISSING.
WHAT?
TOOK THE TUMBLER AND TURNED OFF THE GPS TRACKER.
I ASSUME YOU INSTALLED BACKUP LOCATORS ON ALL THE BATMOBILES? WITHOUT TELLING ANY OF US?
SEARCHING
...
SHE'S HEADED UP ROUTE 1, NEAR THE GOTHAM RIVER.
THAT'S WHAT I THOUGHT.
OPEN 24 HR
"HERE, TAKE YOUR PILLS."

CRASH

...BATMAN?

WORSE.

THWIP

click

BANG

BANG

BANG

BANG

BARBARA.

WHAT ARE YOU THINKING?

"We're ending our arrangement. You've become a liability."

YOU OFTEN CAN'T APPRECIATE HOW **IMPORTANT** SOMEONE IS WHILE THEY'RE STILL ALIVE.

AND ONLY BY THEIR PASSING DO YOU SUDDENLY REALIZE THE **STAGGERING MAGNITUDE** OF WHAT YOU'VE JUST LOST.

RIGHT NOW, THAT'S EXACTLY HOW GOTHAM CITY FEELS ABOUT THE DEATH OF **JIM GORDON.**

JIM WAS THE BEST OF US. HE HAD **COMPASSION** FOR EVERY CITIZEN AND AN EYE TOWARD THE **FUTURE,** AND HE WAS WILLING TO DO WHATEVER IT TOOK TO GET US THERE.

HE WAS A REMINDER THAT THE SMOLDERING CAULDRON OF GOTHAM CITY DOESN'T JUST CREATE VILLAINS LIKE JOKER AND AZRAEL--IT FORGES **HEROES** LIKE JIM GORDON.

FLICK

SAINT

DUMAS

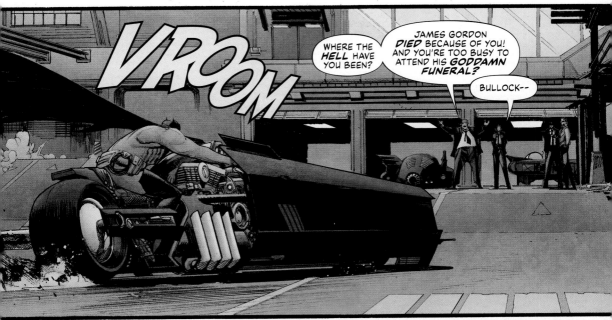

VROOM

WHERE THE **HELL** HAVE YOU BEEN?

JAMES GORDON **DIED** BECAUSE OF YOU! AND YOU'RE TOO BUSY TO ATTEND HIS **GODDAMN** FUNERAL?

BULLOCK--

AND WHAT ABOUT BABS-- WHY DIDN'T YOU **WASTE** AZRAEL WHEN YOU HAD THE CHANCE?!

YOU AND BARBARA WENT ROGUE--**THAT'S** WHY SHE'S IN A WHEELCHAIR! AND THAT'S THE KIND OF RECKLESS BEHAVIOR THAT MIGHT GET YOU SUSPENDED.

HE'S **RIGHT.**

I **SHOULD** HAVE BEEN AT THE FUNERAL.

AFTER EVERYTHING THAT HAPPENED...I...I JUST WASN'T SURE I'D BE **WELCOME.** I DIDN'T WANT TO CAUSE A FIGHT.

I'M SO SORRY. TO **ALL** OF YOU.

YOU KNOW WHAT MADE GORDON A GREAT LEADER? HE UNDERSTOOD TWO THINGS--**TRUST** AND **COMPROMISE.**

HE ACCEPTED THAT THE GOOD GUYS DIDN'T ALWAYS GET ALONG--THEY JUST NEEDED TO TRUST EACH OTHER. AND THAT MOVING FORWARD SOMETIMES MEANT EMBRACING OUR DIFFERENCES.

SO HOW THE HELL DO WE MOVE FORWARD?

BY FOCUSING ON THE **WORK.**

WE'VE ALWAYS BELIEVED THAT GOTHAM BEGAN AS A SMALL VILLAGE ON THE COAST. THAT'S WHY THE JOURNAL'S MAP IS SO STRANGE--IT PLACES THE VILLAGE IN THE **WRONG PLACE**, ON THE EDGE OF A LARGE BAY THAT EXTENDED INLAND. IN AN AREA WE NOW KNOW AS **GOTHAM RESERVOIR.**

BUT THE JOURNAL IS ACCURATE--I FOUND THE LOST SETTLEMENT BENEATH THE RESERVOIR. SOMEONE TRIED TO **ERASE** OUR EARLY HISTORY BY **FLOODING** IT.

WHO?

"EDMOND WAYNE.

"WITH **ARKHAM** DEAD, EDMOND HAD RECLAIMED HIS INHERITANCE. BUT RATHER THAN HONORING HIS PROMISE TO GIVE BAKKAR HALF OF GOTHAM, EDMOND KILLED HIM.

"AS LORD OF GOTHAM, HE CONVINCED THE BRITISH TO HELP HIM PURGE THE ENTIRE VALLEY SO THEY COULD TURN IT INTO ONE OF THE MOST **VALUABLE** PORTS IN THE NEW WORLD.

"HE ERASED ALL EVIDENCE OF BAKKAR AND THE CHAPEL OF **ST. DUMAS** BY DAMMING THE RIVER AND FLOODING THE VALLEY.

"ALL THE VILLAGERS LOST THEIR HOMES. THOSE WHO COULDN'T AFFORD TO LEAVE WERE RESETTLED IN A PLACE WE NOW CALL **BACKPORT.**

"EDMOND REDREW THE COASTLINE AS THE LAND BELOW THE LAKE DRIED UP. THEN HE BUILT A NEW SETTLEMENT BY SELLING PROPERTY TO THE EAST INDIA COMPANY.

"THAT'S THE **TRUTH** ABOUT GOTHAM, ABOUT HOW THE **WAYNE FORTUNE** STARTED IN THE NEW WORLD.

"AND THAT'S WHY JOKER SENT AZRAEL AFTER ME--BY REVIVING THE DESCENDANT OF BAKKAR, JOKER WANTS TO **EXPOSE** THE COVER-UP AND **DESTROY** THE WAYNE LEGACY."

...HE'D WRITTEN ME A LOVE LETTER. A *CRY FOR HELP.* AND HE WROTE IT ON A PLAYING CARD.

THE THREE OF DIAMONDS.

LOOK FAMILIAR?

DON'T GIVE UP ON ME. -J

YOUR COSTUME.

WEARING THE DIAMONDS WAS A WAY TO REMIND MYSELF THAT NO MATTER HOW BAD IT GOT, JACK NAPIER WAS *ALIVE.*

THAT'S WHY I CREATED THE PILLS LAST YEAR--BECAUSE I THOUGHT WE COULD FINALLY BE *JACK* AND *HARLEEN.*

BUT I *FAILED.*

JOKER WAS RIGHT--I'M WEAK. AND I'LL *ALWAYS* BE THE *VICTIM.*

HE'S WRONG.

YOU FELL IN LOVE WITH THE *DEVIL.* AND NOT ONLY DID YOU SURVIVE, YOU CAME OUT STRONGER-- *YOU BEAT HIM.*

AND YOU CAN DO IT AGAIN.

WHAT DO YOU MEAN?

JACK'S STILL *ALIVE*--HE'S TRYING TO REACH OUT.

YOU NEED TO TRY AGAIN. YOU NEED TO BRING HIM BACK--

BUT IT DIDN'T WORK LAST TIME.

BECAUSE *I* WAS THERE. JOKER CAN'T RESIST ME.

BUT...I DON'T THINK I CAN DO IT ALONE.

YOU WON'T BE ALONE...

"...YOU'LL HAVE YOUR *CHILDREN.*"

NEW ARKHAM

WHERE IS HE, JACK? WHERE'S *AZRAEL?*

AND THE MESSAGE WRITTEN IN BLOOD--*WHAT DID IT SAY?*

JESUS, *YOU* AGAIN? THOUGHT I MADE MYSELF CLEAR.

WHERE IS HE?

BATMAN'S NOT COMING.

...

YOU KNOW, I ALWAYS THOUGHT YOU WERE PRETTY *BORING.* MAYBE THAT'S WHY I KEPT YOU AROUND-- BECAUSE IT MADE *ME* FEEL THAT MUCH MORE *HILARIOUS.*

BUT I NEVER THOUGHT YOU WERE THIS *STUPID.*

WHY THE HELL WOULD YOU EVER RISK BRINGING YOUR CHILDREN--WHAT'S TO STOP ME FROM ESCAPING AND KIDNAPPING--

YOU WON'T.

AND WHY'S THAT?

BECAUSE *JACK* WOULDN'T LET YOU.

THEY'RE SO **BEAUTIFUL**, HARLEY.

I'M SO SORRY I COULDN'T BE THERE.

IT'S OKAY. I HAD BATMAN.

HE WAS ACTUALLY THE ONE WHO **DELIVERED** THEM--HAD A BIT OF AN EMERGENCY WHILE INVESTIGATING LAFFY--

BATMAN DELIVERED MY CHILDREN?!

BORN EXACTLY WHERE JOKER WAS BORN-- AT LAFFY'S GRAVE?!

JESUS, IF THAT ISN'T DRIPPING WITH IRONY, MAYBE THERE REALLY IS A CURSE.

I KNOW THERE'S MORE GOING ON HERE THAN WE REALIZE-- YOU NEED TO HELP US!

I CAN'T-- JOKER KNOWS EVERYTHING I KNOW, BUT IT DOESN'T ALWAYS WORK THE OTHER WAY!

BATMAN HELPED YOU REACH HIM BEFORE. HERE-- TAKE MY HAND.

WHERE'S AZRAEL?

I DON'T KNOW!

CONCENTRATE. HE'S A GIANT RELIGIOUS NUT WITH A BIG FLAMING SWORD.

FLAMING SWORD...

FWOOSS

WAIT...

...I REMEMBER A FLAMING CROSS.

...A SWORD LODGED IN A POOL OF HOLY OIL.

GOOD.

SOME OLD CHURCH WITH A GIANT STAINED GLASS WINDOW...

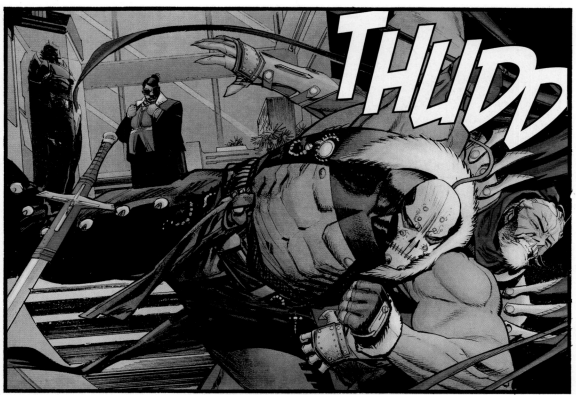

THUDD

YOU KNOW I NEVER UNDERSTOOD WHY JOKER WOULD WANT A HOMELESS, CANCEROUS JESUS FREAK TO GO AFTER SOMEONE AS TOUGH AS *BATMAN.*

BUT THEN I REALIZED JOKER DIDN'T EXPECT YOU TO *WIN*--HE JUST WANTED YOU TO SURVIVE LONG ENOUGH TO UPEND EVERYTHING ABOUT *BRUCE WAYNE.*

SO I HIRED BANE--TO TAKE OVER WHEN YOU *FAILED.*

THOKK

MERCENARIES ARE *WEAK*--THEY ONLY WORSHIP MONEY.

BLAM BLAM BLAM BLAM

YOU THINK I'M WEAK?

THEN LET'S TURN UP THE *JUICE* A LITTLE.

CRASH

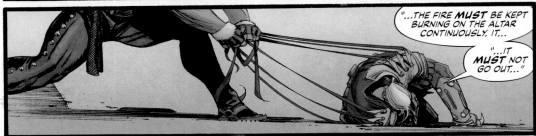

"...THE FIRE **MUST** BE KEPT BURNING ON THE ALTAR CONTINUOUSLY. IT...

"...IT **MUST** NOT GO OUT..."

HAHA--YOUR **FAITH** IS YOUR **WEAKNESS**.

GOD WILL **SAVE** ME...

GOD CAN DO WHATEVER HE WANTS WITH YOU...

...AFTER I BREAK YOU.

THUK

ARGH!

I'VE KNOWN MANY MERCENARIES-- THEY WERE PRIDE- FUL AND TOOK UNNECESSARY RISKS...

ARRRRGGHHHHH!

...AND OFTEN LEFT THEMSELVES *EXPOSED.*

FWGOSH!

THE EXPOSED TUBE IS A CHALLENGE TO MY ENEMIES...TO COME IN CLOSE IF THEY DARE TO CUT IT.

CHALLENGE ACCEPTED.

HACK

DID IT WORK?

YOU WERE RIGHT. JACK'S *ALIVE.*

AND HE TOLD ME WHERE JOKER FOUND AZRAEL.

NEW ARKHAM

GOOD WORK.

WHAT ABOUT THE MESSAGE ON THE WALL?

...

HE DOESN'T KNOW.

BUT JACK SAID HE'LL TRY TO HELP US IN OTHER WAYS.

HOW?

I DON'T KNOW--WE'LL JUST HAVE TO WAIT AND SEE.

HOW CAN WE TRUST HIM?

YOU DON'T HAVE TO TRUST *HIM,* BATS...

...JUST TRUST *ME.*

SHSHH

SHHSHH

SSLSH

SHKK

CLEARING OUT THE COMPETITION, I SEE.

HOW'D YOU GET PAST SECURITY?

THEY LET ME WALK RIGHT IN.

AND WHY WOULD THEY DO THAT?

BECAUSE...

"Here I was worried this would be too easy."

THEY SERIOUSLY LET YOU WALK THROUGH THE FRONT DOOR JUST BECAUSE YOU WERE DRESSED LIKE *CYBER-METAL BATMAN?*

DIDN'T EVEN *RAISE AN EYEBROW,* HUH?

OH.

I SEE YOU BROUGHT WILLOW UFGOOD WITH YOU.

YOU DON'T HAVE MUCH TIME--I DISABLED THE ALARM AND JAMMED THEIR PHONES, BUT I CAN'T STOP THEM FROM BREAKING DOWN THE DOOR.

WE CAN MANAGE.

BE CAREFUL-- THIS GUN IS A *CLASSIC!*

SHOVE!

LITTLE SURPRISED TO SEE YOU HELPING, *JERVIS--*

NO HARD FEELINGS ABOUT WHAT HAPPENED LAST YEAR WITH CLAYFACE AND *WHAT'S- HER-FACE?*

HER NAME IS *MARIAN DREWS!*

AH-- SO *THAT'S* WHY YOU'RE HERE.

DON'T WAIT FOR US--WE'LL FIND OUR OWN RABBIT HOLE.

HATTER, WAIT.

--WHY'D YOU CALL ME OUT TO A FIRE?

POLICE FOUND TWO BODIES.

SO LET *THEM* HANDLE IT--THE GTO HAS MORE IMPORTANT--

THE FIRST BODY IS *BANE.*

WHAT?!

SOMEONE TOOK HIS HEAD OFF.

OH MY GOD. AND THE SECOND BODY?

RUTH REDFORD.

SO WE FINALLY UNCOVERED THE ELUSIVE *RUTH.*

GIANT FIRE, DECAPITATION-- DEFINITELY AZRAEL'S M.O.

WONDER WHY THEY TURNED ON EACH OTHER.

DON'T KNOW YET, BUT CHECK THIS OUT...

HER HARD DRIVE MANAGED TO SURVIVE THE FIRE. FOUND SOME INTERESTING FILES ON IT, INCLUDING BLUEPRINTS FOR A *MECHANIZED BAT-SUIT* THAT AZRAEL STOLE.

FANTASTIC-- AND HERE I WAS WORRIED THIS WOULD BE *TOO EASY.*

ALSO HAS A LIST OF HER CLIENTS.

THE NAMES AND ADDRESSES OF *ALL* THE *ELITES.*

SEE ANYONE WE KNOW?

OH JESUS...

"WHERE'S AZRAEL?"

I HAVEN'T SEEN HIM SINCE *THE JOKER* GOT TO HIM.

AND WHY SHOULD I BELIEVE YOU?

IF I KNEW, I'D TELL YOU, *BRUCE.*

JEAN-PAUL IS VERY DANGERO AND HE NEEDS BE STOPPED.

WHO ARE YOU?

I'M A KNIGHT OF THE ORDER OF ST. DUMAS--A HISTORIAN AND A COLLECTOR.

WHEN I LEARNED THE JOKER FOUND THE JOURNAL, I KNEW I HAD TO TAKE IT FROM HIM. I FEARED HE WOULD USE IT TO EXPOSE THE TRUTH ABOUT GOTHAM'S *CURSE,* AND I COULDN'T LET HIM DISRUPT THE PEACE YOUR FAMILY CREATED.

BUT I FAILED. AND NOW JEAN-PAUL IS ON THE *WARPATH.*

YOU HAVE NO *CONTROL* OVER HIM?

NOT ANYMORE. NOT AFTER HE LEARNED THAT WE'VE BEEN LYING TO HIS FAMILY FOR *CENTURIES.*

HOW LONG HAVE YOU KNOWN HIM?

"BUT BAKKAR WOULDN'T GO QUIETLY. HE WANTED VENGEANCE.

"HE WANTED TO SEIZE POWER BY FINDING THE *LAST WAYNE*.

"ONCE THEY ARRIVED HERE, BAKKAR SET HIS PLAN INTO MOTION.

"IN ORDER TO OVERTHROW THE CRIMINAL EMPIRE OF GOTHAM, BAKKAR INSISTED THEY POSE AS CRIMINALS THEMSELVES.

"THEY BECAME THIEVES AND SMUGGLERS, GETTING TO KNOW EVERY PIRATE AND KIDNAPPER WHO PASSED THROUGH GOTHAM.

"THEY STUDIED THEM, LEARNED THEIR WEAKNESSES...

"...AND GOT CLOSE WITH THEM.

"IT WASN'T LONG BEFORE EDMOND FELL UNDER GOTHAM'S SPELL. THAT'S WHAT THIS VALLEY DOES TO PEOPLE--IT *SEDUCES* THEM.

"FOR TWO YEARS, BAKKAR WAITED--BIDING HIS TIME AND ALLOWING EDMOND'S HEART TO BECOME AS DARK AS THE MEN THEY SWORE TO OVERTHROW.

"ONCE EDMOND'S TRANSFORMATION WAS COMPLETE, THERE WAS ONLY ONE THING LEFT FOR BAKKAR TO DO..."

"...TURN HIM INTO *A KILLER*.

"IT WAS THE ONLY WAY TO RECLAIM GOTHAM-- BY *ELIMINATING* EVERYONE WHO STOOD IN THEIR WAY.

"THEY STARTED AT THE DOCKS AND WORKED THEIR WAY UP TO THE HIGHEST CLIFF--THE HOME OF *LAFFY ARKHAM*...

"...THE *VAMPIRE OF GOTHAM VALLEY*.

SHUNK

"WITH LAFAYETTE GONE, THE TWO MEN WERE SUPPOSED TO DIVIDE THE VALLEY IN HALF..."

VROOO

WHAT HAPPENED?

...AZRAEL... NO WARNING...

HE AND JOKER KILLED OVER A *DOZEN* INMATES AT NEW ARKHAM.

THEN THEY CAME HERE--HIT US WITH RPGS BEFORE BREAKING THROUGH SECURITY. AZRAEL PINNED US DOWN WHILE JOKER *SNATCHED THE TWINS.*

I MANAGED TO DROP GABRIEL BEFORE THE BUILDING COLLAPSED.

WHERE'S HARLEY?

¿...COUGH... COUGH...¿

GRRR... PANT PANT...

MEDIC!

TRY TO BREATHE.

...HE TOOK THEM...HE TOOK MY BABIES...

JACK WAS SUPPOSED TO STOP HIM--SAID HE WOULDN'T LET THIS HAPPEN!

BROKEN RIBS--LIE DOWN AND LET--

I DON'T WANT TO LIE DOWN--*I WANT TO GET MY CHILDREN BACK!*

I'LL FIND THEM, HARLEY--

I'M COMING *WITH* YOU!

NO! YOU NEED MEDICAL--

DON'T ARGUE WITH ME, BATMAN--THIS IS ALL *YOUR* FAULT!

WHAT?!

YOU THINK I WANTED TO PUT UP WITH MORE OF JOKER'S *HUMILIATING ABUSE?*

TO BE REMINDED HOW STUPID AND *BLIND* I WAS FOR ALL THOSE YEARS?

YOU THINK I WANTED TO RISK *EXPOSING* MY *CHILDREN* TO HIM? *NO!*

BUT YOU SHOWED UP LOOKING FOR MY HELP--SO I GAVE IT. *KNOW WHY?*

BECAUSE *I CARE ABOUT YOU!*

MAYBE BECAUSE I LIKE LEATHER MASKS, OR MAYBE I GOT A THING FOR SCREWED-UP MEN--

--ALL I KNOW IS I DID WHATEVER YOU ASKED *AND IT COST ME EVERYTHING!*

I AIN'T *ASKING* YOU ANYTHING-- *I'M TELLING YOU.*

TAKE ME TO ARKHAM AND HELP ME GET MY BABIES BACK!

SUIT UP.

THE BAT-SIGNAL?

AZRAEL. IT'S COMING FROM *OLD ARKHAM.*

WE'LL BE RIGHT BEHIND YOU.

TRACKING MODE

SEARCHING...

TINK

DANGER!

SHIT.

FLASH GRENADE 44J

BANG

WHUD

"JACK, I KNOW YOU CAN HEAR ME..."

...HE wants to **MURDER** our **CHILDREN**, JACK! WE NEED TO FIGHT HIM **TOGETHER.**

THIS ISN'T ABOUT JACK. IT'S ABOUT **YOU** AND **ME.**

THERE IS NO YOU AND ME, **JOKER.**

THIS PART OF ARKHAM HAS SPECIAL MEANING FOR ME-- IT'S WHERE I FIRST MET **HARLEEN QUINZEL.**

A VIRTUOUS YOUNG WOMAN WHO WOULD TURN THIS PLACE AROUND. IF YOU COULD CURE THE JOKER, YOU COULD CURE **ANYONE.**

AND THAT'S WHY I MADE YOU INTO **HARLEY QUINN**--I TOOK THEIR GREATEST HOPE...

...AND TURNED YOU INTO THEIR BIGGEST EMBARRASSMENT-- AN **INMATE.**

I DID CURE YOU. **AND THEN I BEAT YOU.**

YOU DIDN'T BEAT ME. **NAPIER** DID.

YOU COULDN'T HAVE DONE IT ALONE.

THAT'S WHY YOU KEEP ALIGNING YOURSELF WITH POWERFUL MEN... ME, NAPIER, AND NOW **BATMAN**...

STOP IT!

...BECAUSE YOU'RE **WEAK.**

AND NOW YOUR CHILDREN CAN SEE FOR THEMSELVES HOW **HELPLESS** THEIR MOTHER REALLY IS.

÷GASP!÷

"...THAT BAKKAR WAS AN IMPOSTOR!"

ARGH!

SHUCK

THAT'S WHY I'M ALWAYS SMILING, BATMAN! BECAUSE OF THE JOKE I WAS TOLD IN EDMOND'S TOMB.

THAT GOTHAM'S GREATEST HERO IS DESCENDED FROM CRIMINALS!

THAT YOU'RE USING A STOLEN FORTUNE TO WAGE A WAR ON CRIME THAT YOUR FAMILY HELPED CREATE!

DON'T YOU GET IT, BRUCE? YOU'RE NOT REALLY A WAYNE...

AZRAEL IS!

YOUR REIGN IS OVER--I'M TAKING IT ALL BACK.

...FROM YOU AND THE REST OF THE ELITES--

BWAHAHA-HAHA!

WHUD

"In Gotham, no one is above the law."

THE WAYNES WERE ALWAYS GUARDIANS, GOING ALL THE WAY BACK TO THE MIDDLE AGES.

THEY WERE **NOBLES**, USING THEIR WEALTH TO DEFEND THE PEOPLE WHO SHARED THEIR LAND. THEY FOUGHT OFF ANYONE WHO THREATENED THE PEACE.

I ALWAYS WANTED TO HONOR THAT TRADITION HERE IN GOTHAM.

YOU WANTED TO BE A **KNIGHT**.

LEARNING THE TRUTH ABOUT EDMOND HAS BEEN **DIFFICULT** FOR ME.

I WAS PREPARED TO ACCEPT THAT THE **WAYNES HAD SECRETS**, AND THAT MAYBE THEIR PAST WASN'T AS VIRTUOUS AS I'D IMAGINED--

--BUT I NEVER ONCE CONSIDERED THAT **I WASN'T A WAYNE TO BEGIN WITH.**

THAT'S THE TRUE MEANING OF THE **BLOOD MESSAGE.**

DNA TEST CONFIRMS IT-- AZRAEL'S A DESCENDANT OF WHOEVER WROTE THESE WORDS--

--"I AM EDMOND WAYNE."

YOU KNEW?

YOU WERE RIGHT--I **WAS** KEEPING SOMETHING FROM YOU. JACK AND I WERE WORRIED WHAT THE **TRUTH** MIGHT DO TO YOU.

I KNEW YOU'D EVENTUALLY FIGURE IT OUT. AND THAT THERE WAS NOTHING I COULD DO TO STOP IT...

...EXCEPT **BE THERE** FOR YOU.

JOKER'S RIGHT--**THERE IS A CURSE IN GOTHAM.**

ME.

THAT'S BULLSHIT!

WAS YOUR **FATHER A CURSE?** WAS YOUR **MOTHER?** THEY'RE NOT RESPONSIBLE FOR SOMETHING THEY NEVER EVEN KNEW ABOUT, AND **NEITHER ARE YOU!**

WHO CARES IF YOU'RE NOT TECHNICALLY A WAYNE! YOU'RE STILL DOING WHAT THEY'VE ALWAYS DONE--GUARDING THE CITY, USING YOUR FORTUNE TO PROTECT THE PEOPLE--

NOT ACCORDING TO THIS.

A LIST OF THE ELITES--THE GTO FINALLY FOUND RUTH. OR WHAT WAS LEFT OF HER.

THESE ARE THE NAMES OF **EVERY BUSINESS** AND **EVERY INVESTOR** SHE'S EVER MADE A DIME FOR.

SO?

MOST OF IT'S CHANNELED THROUGH ONE COMPANY--THE LARGEST COMPANY IN GOTHAM.

WAYNE-CORP.

WHUD

BLARF!

TURN.

LAST ONE.

SHIT.

FOR DECADES, IT'S BEEN MY **HONOR TO SERVE YOU.** FIGHTING CRIME, SAVING LIVES, TRYING TO MAKE THIS A BETTER PLACE.

BUT I KNEW IT COULDN'T GO ON FOREVER--IT'S CLEAR TO ME NOW THAT THE ERA OF BATMAN MUST **COME TO AN END.**

WEARING THIS CAPE WAS A SIMPLE IDEA, BORN IN A SIMPLER TIME--AT FIRST I JUST WANTED TO HELP CATCH THE **BAD GUYS.**

BUT OVER THE YEARS THINGS HAVE GOTTEN MORE COMPLICATED. IT'S NO LONGER A CHILDISH GAME OF COPS AND ROBBERS--IT'S SERIAL KILLERS, MONSTERS, AND SUPER-CRIMINALS.

WHEN I STARTED OUT, ALL I NEEDED TO CATCH THEM WAS ROPE AND HANDCUFFS, BUT NOW I'M A ONE-MAN ARMY WHO DOES AS MUCH DAMAGE TO YOU AS I DO TO **THEM.** I USED TO BE A HERO FROM THE GOLDEN AGE, **BUT NOW I'M A VILLAIN.**

AND THAT'S WHY JACK NAPIER BEAT ME, BY SAYING WHAT I WAS AFRAID TO ADMIT.

THAT'S WHY I'M SUPPORTING THE **NAPIER INITIATIVE.**

BEING BATMAN MEANS BEING WHATEVER GOTHAM NEEDS ME TO BE, AND WHAT YOU ALL NEED NOW **IS TO KNOW THE TRUTH...**

...THAT BATMAN IS REALLY **BRUCE WAYNE.**

LIVE

I RECENTLY LEARNED THAT THE WAYNE EMPIRE HAS BEEN HIJACKED BY THOSE WHO HAVE CORRUPTED GOTHAM THE MOST--BY THE ELITES.

WHICH MAKES ME COMPLICIT IN THEIR CRIMES, WHICH MAKES ME **EVEN MORE** RESPONSIBLE FOR CRIMINALS LIKE JOKER AND AZRAEL.

LIVE

THAT'S WHY I'M GIVING IT ALL AWAY--TO DESTROY THE **ELITES** AND GIVE GOTHAM BACK TO THE PEOPLE. MY FORTUNE DOESN'T BELONG TO ME--IT BELONGS TO **YOU.**

WAYNECORP AND ALL OF ITS SUBSIDIARIES WILL BE DISSOLVED.

MY ENTIRE INHERITANCE WILL BE PUT INTO A NONPROFIT THAT WILL CREATE BETTER SCHOOLS, LIBRARIES, HOMELESS SHELTERS, AND SCHOLARSHIPS. EVERYTHING WE GENERATE WILL BE DONATED RIGHT BACK TO GOTHAM, **OFFSETTING YOUR TAXES FOR DECADES.**

GOTHAM WILL NO LONGER BE A CITY OF DARKNESS-- IT WILL BE A CITY OF LIGHT. IT WILL BE A PLACE WITHOUT SHADOWS...

...A PLACE **WITHOUT** BATMAN.

BUT FIRST, **I NEED A FAVOR.**

AZRAEL'S STILL OUT THERE. AS SOON AS THE SUN GOES DOWN, HE'LL MAKE HIS MOVE.

I CAN GET HIM. BUT I DON'T WANT ANYONE ELSE GETTING HURT.

THAT'S WHY I'M ASKING YOU ALL TO **STAY OFF THE STREETS** UNTIL I CAN CATCH HIM.

I'M ASKING FOR YOUR **FORGIVE-NESS.**

I'M ASKING YOU TO **TRUST ME.**

I'M ASKING FOR YOUR PERMISSION TO BE BATMAN **ONE LAST TIME.**

WE NEED UNITS STATIONED AT EVERY HOSPITAL IN GOTHAM.

WITH RUTH DEAD, AZRAEL WILL NEED A NEW SOURCE OF MEDICATION, SO THOSE WILL LIKELY BE HIS TARGETS.

WAY AHEAD OF YOU.

WE NEED TO CLOSE DOWN THE AIRPORTS, SUBWAYS, AND ANY ROAD LEADING OUT OF GOTHAM.

ON IT.

KEEP AN EYE ON EVERY SECURITY CAMERA THROUGHOUT THE CITY.

GOT A BUNCH OF KIDS IN BACKPORT ON LOOKOUT-- TURNED NAPIER'S LIBRARY INTO A COMMAND CENTER.

HOW ABOUT YOU--SURE YOU'RE UP FOR THIS?

I CAN STEP ON A GAS PEDAL, IF THAT'S WHAT YOU'RE ASKING.

GOOD.

GARAGE

AND WHAT'LL YOU BE DOING?

I'LL BE IN THE BATMOBILE.

AZRAEL DESTROYED MOST OF THEM WHEN HE ATTACKED THE GTO, SO THERE'S ONLY ONE LEFT.

BA-VROOM

BRUCE, WAIT. WHAT HAPPENS WHEN YOU CATCH AZRAEL?

ARE YOU GOING TO BRING HIM IN SAFELY AND LET HIM SERVE HIS TIME? OR DO YOU HAVE SOMETHING *ELSE* IN MIND?

WHAT ARE YOU SAYING?

YOU KNOW WHAT I'M SAYING.

...

THAT'S WHAT I THOUGHT.

IT'S NOT WORTH IT, BRUCE. YOU WON'T BE ABLE TO LIVE WITH YOUR-SELF. *BATMAN DOESN'T KILL.*

BATMAN'S DEAD...

...AND SO IS AZRAEL.

"God put us on different paths, but we ended up in the same place, didn't we?"

VROOM

WE HAVE VISUAL ON *AZRAEL!*

HE'S ON THE *ROOFTOPS* WEST OF THE PARK, RIGHT ALONG THE HIGHWAY!

I BET HE'S HEADED TO THE AIRPORT NEAR THE COAST GUARD STATION.

HE'S GOTTA COME DOWN FROM THE ROOFTOPS AT SOME POINT!

BRUCE, STAY BEHIND THE OTHERS IN CASE AZRAEL DOUBLES BACK.

...

BRUCE-- *YOU THERE?*

HE JUST LANDED! *I'VE GOT HIM--*

WHUD

BOOP

VVVVVVVVVVVVVVVVVW PKK PKK PKK

WAIT, SOMETHING'S WRONG WITH MY CAR!

MINE TOO! WHAT'S GOING ON?!

DAMMIT!

NOT THIS SHIT AGAIN!

FWOOSH

WHAT HAPPENED?

HE TAMPERED WITH OUR CARS. ADDED SOME KIND OF *SHUT-OFF DEVICE.*

HE WAS ONLY *USING US* TO HELP FIND AZRAEL!

COMMISSIONER-- WE'VE GOT A PROBLEM--

REMOTE DISRUPTER. *I KNEW IT!*

WHY WOULD HE DO THAT?

SNAP

BA-VROOM

BECAUSE HE DOESN'T WANT US STOPPING HIM...

FWOOOSH

IIIIRt

CRASH

FWOOSH

VROOOOOOM

NICE TRY,
BRUCE.

I THOUGHT BATMAN *DIDN'T KILL.*

ISN'T THAT WHAT MAKES US *DIFFERENT?*

BUDDA BUDDA BUDDA

BUDDA BUDDA BUDDA

THOKK

HUKK

WELL IF YOU'RE NO LONGER BATMAN, AND YOU'RE NO LONGER A WAYNE, THEN *WHO ARE YOU?*

I'M YOUR RECKONING.

NO. I KNOW WHAT YOU *REALLY ARE,* BRUCE...

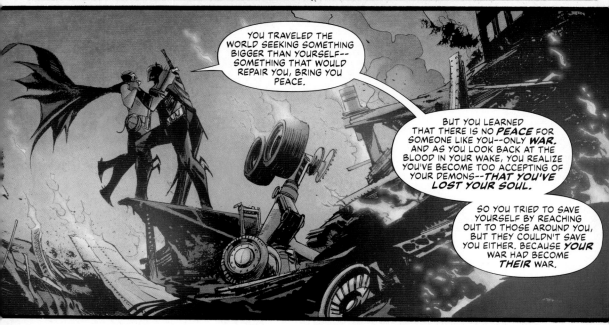

YOU TRAVELED THE WORLD SEEKING SOMETHING BIGGER THAN YOURSELF-- SOMETHING THAT WOULD REPAIR YOU, BRING YOU PEACE.

BUT YOU LEARNED THAT THERE IS NO *PEACE* FOR SOMEONE LIKE YOU--ONLY *WAR.* AND AS YOU LOOK BACK AT THE BLOOD IN YOUR WAKE, YOU REALIZE YOU'VE BECOME TOO ACCEPTING OF YOUR DEMONS--*THAT YOU'VE LOST YOUR SOUL.*

SO YOU TRIED TO SAVE YOURSELF BY REACHING OUT TO THOSE AROUND YOU, BUT THEY COULDN'T SAVE YOU EITHER. BECAUSE *YOUR* WAR HAD BECOME *THEIR* WAR.

NOW HERE YOU ARE, ALL ALONE, TRYING TO BE A MARTYR...

...IN A BATTLE THAT KILLED YOU A LONG TIME AGO.

I KNOW YOU, BRUCE.

...GO TO HELL...

YOU'RE ME.

WE'RE BROTHERS, LIKE CAIN AND ABEL. NOT BOUND BY BLOOD, BUT BY DESTINY.

GOD PUT US ON DIFFERENT PATHS, BUT WE ENDED UP IN THE SAME PLACE, DIDN'T WE?

THE CITY WILL FIGHT YOU. EVEN AFTER I'M GONE.

THERE WON'T BE A CITY LEFT. NOT AFTER THE FLOOD...

CRAKK

ALL UNITS REPORT TO THE ABANDONED AIRPORT DEPOT.

GRAYSON--YOU STILL HAVE EYES ON AZRAEL?

NEGATIVE.

BUT HE CAN'T BE FAR--I HIT HIM PRETTY HARD.

‹HRRNNF›

BRUCE... IS THAT A GUN?

GODDAMN IT--WHAT ARE YOU DOING? THIS ISN'T YOU!

AZRAEL NEEDS TO DIE. FOR WHAT HE'S DONE, FOR WHAT HE STANDS FOR.

AND WHAT IF IT KILLS YOU?!

MAYBE THAT'S FOR THE BEST. MAYBE THAT'S WHAT GOTHAM REALLY NEEDS--A CLEAN SLATE.

JESUS, YOU HAVEN'T LEARNED ANYTHING, HAVE YOU?! AFTER EVERYTHING THAT'S HAPPENED, NOTHING'S CHANGED!

GORDON IS DEAD. BARBARA BARELY SURVIVED. AZRAEL IS RIGHT--I BROUGHT THIS WAR UPON YOU.

SO IT WAS ALL A MISTAKE? BRINGING US INTO THIS? BARBARA, JASON, GORDON--

YES.

THEN WHY DID YOU DO IT, BRUCE?

DO WHAT?

WHY ADOPT ME IN THE FIRST PLACE?

I'VE RUINED YOUR LIFE, DICK.

YOU SAVED ME!

I TRIED TO SAVE YOU AND I FAILED--BECAUSE I'M NOT MUCH OF A FATHER.

MAYBE NOT...

...BUT YOU'RE **MY** FATHER.

AND I STILL **BELIEVE IN YOU.**

DON'T END IT THIS WAY--DON'T MAKE ME WATCH YOU--

YOU'VE ALWAYS BEEN SMART ENOUGH TO SEE MY FLAWS, DICK. MAYBE THAT'S WHY THERE'S BEEN A WEDGE BETWEEN US-- BECAUSE **WE BOTH KNOW WHO THE BETTER MAN IS.**

NOW STEP ASIDE AND LET ME **END THIS.**

FINE, BUT END IT **YOUR WAY.**

NOT AS AZRAEL...

...AS **BATMAN.**

GRAYSON, WHAT THE HELL IS GOING ON?

SEND UNITS TO THE DAM AT GOTHAM RESERVOIR.

THE RESERVOIR?

AZRAEL IS GOING TO TRY TO DESTROY IT.

NO TIME FOR EVACUATION--GET PEOPLE OFF THE STREETS AND INTO THE BUILDINGS.

HOLY BIBLICAL FLOOD, BATMAN.

COMMISSIONER, CALL THE NATIONAL GUARD--

VROOM

THAT WAS GCPD.

ABOUT TIME.

AZRAEL MIGHT BE ON THE BASE. NOTIFY YOUR MEN AND START SWEEPING THE AREA.

GET THE HELO INTO THE AIR--HEAD STRAIGHT TO THE RESERVOIR. I'LL STIR UP MORE SUPPORT.

ON IT.

COMMANDER-- PUT GOTHAM INTERNATIONAL ON LOCKDOWN!

CLICK

U.S. COAST GUARD

÷GASP÷

JESUS CHRIST.

BREAKING

THREAT TO GOTHAM RESERVOIR. CITYWIDE FLOOD?

HE'S GOING TO FLOOD GOTHAM?

OH MY GOD...

RUMBLE RUMBLE

FWOOOSH

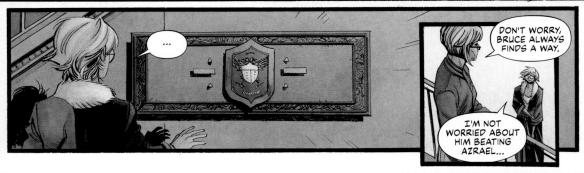

...

DON'T WORRY, BRUCE ALWAYS FINDS A WAY.

I'M NOT WORRIED ABOUT HIM BEATING AZRAEL...

"HE'S LOST **EVERYTHING**: HIS HOME, HIS INHERITANCE, THE HONOR OF HIS FAMILY LEGACY. THERE'S ONLY ONE THING AZRAEL HASN'T TAKEN FROM HIM: **HIS SOUL.**

"THAT'S THE ONLY THING KEEPING BRUCE FROM FALLING INTO THE **ABYSS.** I JUST HOPE HE CAN SAVE HIMSELF...

"...BY REMEMBERING **WHO HE REALLY IS.**"

MY FIRST ORDER AS COMMISSIONER WAS TO INSTALL THIS SIGNAL.

YOU'RE OKAY WORKING WITH A VIGILANTE?

I KNOW YOU WON'T BE WEARING THE MASK FOR-EVER.

IF YOU WANT TO HONOR YOUR PARENTS, WORK HARD TO MAKE THEM **PROUD.**

I BELIEVE THAT IF WE FIGHT **HARD ENOUGH,** WE CAN MAKE GOTHAM A PLACE WHERE HEROES DON'T HAVE TO HIDE ANYMORE.

THAT'S HOW I'LL KNOW WE'VE WON--THE DAY THAT MASK **COMES OFF.**

JAMES GORDON

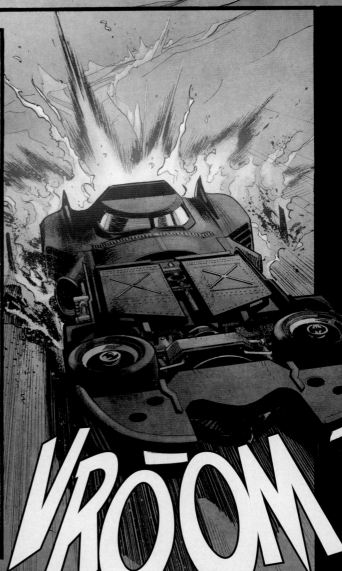

...IT'S BECAUSE I *FORCED YOU TO KILL ME!*

CLANG

SHIELDS.

WHUD

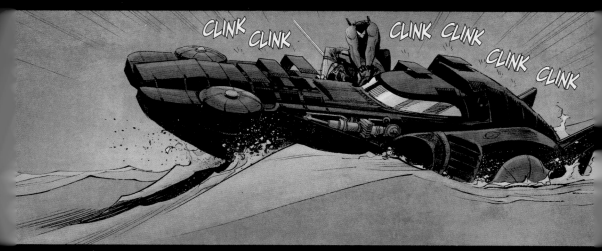

CLINK CLINK   CLINK CLINK   CLINK CLINK

CLANG

ARRRRRRRRGH!

:HNNF:

SHUK

SHUK

SHUK

TELL ME ONE LAST THING BEFORE THIS IS OVER: *DO YOU THINK THEY KNEW?*

WHO?

YOUR PARENTS?

DID THEY KNOW THEY WERE *SWINE* DRAPED IN *PEARLS?* LEECHES FEEDING FROM THE *BLOODY TIT OF GOTHAM?* FAKE ARISTOCRATS BRED FROM A *ROTTEN* BLOODLINE?

HACK

...GRRRGLE...

SNIFF

DETECTIVE.

GOOD LUCK, COWL HEAD.

DUKE. YOU'D HAVE MADE A GREAT ROBIN.

HA.

COMMISSIONER.

NOT SURE WHY YOU'RE LETTING US DO THIS, BRUCE.

WHAT'S YOUR ANGLE?

HARLEY? WHAT ARE YOU DOING?

YOU *KNOW* WHAT I'M DOING, BATS.

I JUST LOST JACK. *I'M NOT LOSING YOU TOO.*

YOU DON'T WANT TO DO THIS. THINK OF YOUR KIDS, THINK OF YOUR FUTURE TOGETHER.

LOCK

NO. I CAN'T...

...I CAN'T BE ALONE.

YOU'RE NOT ALONE. YOU'RE JUST FEELING LOST.

...

BELIEVE ME, I KNOW THE DIFFERENCE.

HARLEY, I WANT TO THANK YOU FOR EVERYTHING YOU DID FOR ME.

WITHOUT YOUR HELP, THIS WHOLE THING MIGHT HAVE ENDED VERY DIFFERENTLY.

YOU GUIDED ME OUT OF THE DARKNESS-- HELPED ME FIND A PATH TO REDEMPTION AND CHANGE GOTHAM IN WAYS I NEVER THOUGHT POSSIBLE.

YOU *SAVED MY SOUL.*

WELL, I GUESS I WAS RETURNING THE FAVOR.

I'M NOT GOING ANYWHERE, I PROMISE.

IF YOU NEED SOMETHING, YOU KNOW WHERE TO FIND ME.

UNLOCK

UM... EVERYTHING OKAY HERE?

EVERY-THING IS FINE.

NICE UNIFORM.

"WHILE THE TOTAL VALUE OF BRUCE WAYNE'S ASSETS HAS YET TO BE DETERMINED, MOST ARE ESTIMATING IT TO BE IN THE HUNDREDS OF BILLIONS."

"AND AS PROMISED, MR. WAYNE HAS BEGUN *GIVING IT ALL AWAY.*

"THIS UNPRECEDENTED MOVE WILL STRIKE A MASSIVE BLOW TO THE SO-CALLED *ELITES*, BOOST THE *NAPIER INITIATIVE*, AND HELP THE PEOPLE WHO NEED IT THE MOST--*THE LOWER AND MIDDLE CLASS.*

"OVERSEEING THE TRANSFER IS *LUCIUS FOX*--THE CEO OF WAYNE ENTERPRISE IS RESTRUCTURING THE COMPANY AND MANY OF ITS SUBSIDIARIES INTO NONPROFIT CHARITIES DESIGNED TO INFUSE THE CITY WITH NEW OPPORTUNITIES.

"A LARGE PORTION OF THE MONEY HAS ALSO BEEN DONATED TO THE GCPD WHERE IT'LL BE USED TO GIVE THE POLICE SOME BADLY NEEDED UPGRADES, INCLUDING A FLEET OF SPECIALIZED VEHICLES UNOFFICIALLY CALLED *BATMOBILES.*

"THEY'RE ALSO PLANNING TO REBUILD AND EXPAND THE GTO. NEWLY PROMOTED *SERGEANT BULLOCK* HAS ANNOUNCED PLANS TO RECRUIT *EVEN MORE VIGILANTES* IN THE COMING MONTHS.

"WHILE MOST OF GOTHAM SEEMS VERY PLEASED WITH MR. WAYNE'S DECISION, HE'S NOT WITHOUT HIS CRITICS.

"SOME ARE ACCUSING WAYNE OF *SOCIALISM* AND OF *MILITARIZING THE POLICE*, WHILE OTHERS DON'T THINK HIS DONATIONS *GO FAR ENOUGH.*

"AND OTHERS ARE HAVING A HARD TIME BELIEVING HE WAS EVER REALLY THE VIGILANTE *IN THE FIRST PLACE.*

"BUT THERE IS ONE THING THAT UNITES US, ONE THING WE'RE ALL FEELING: *THE LOSS OF BATMAN.*

"WHATEVER OPINION YOU MIGHT HAVE OF THE *DARK KNIGHT*, HE'S BEEN A HUGE PART OF GOTHAM'S IDENTITY.

"WITHOUT BATMAN, WHAT KIND OF CITY WILL GOTHAM BE? THAT'S THE QUESTION WE'LL BE ASKING OURSELVES A LOT IN THE COMING MONTHS...

"...AS WE BEGIN *THE TRIAL OF BRUCE WAYNE.*"

WHY AM I HERE, BRUCE?

MONTOYA NEEDED SOMEONE TO KEEP AN EYE ON ME, SOMEONE WHO KNOWS MY TRICKS AND CAN STOP ME FROM ESCAPING. SO I HAD HER TRACK YOU DOWN--

NO CELL CAN HOLD YOU, BRUCE. *WE BOTH KNOW THAT.*

YOU REALLY EXPECT ME TO BELIEVE THAT YOU INTEND ON STAYING HERE?

THERE'S GOT TO BE ANOTHER REASON.

YOU'RE RIGHT. THERE IS...

I WANT TO TALK.

TODD

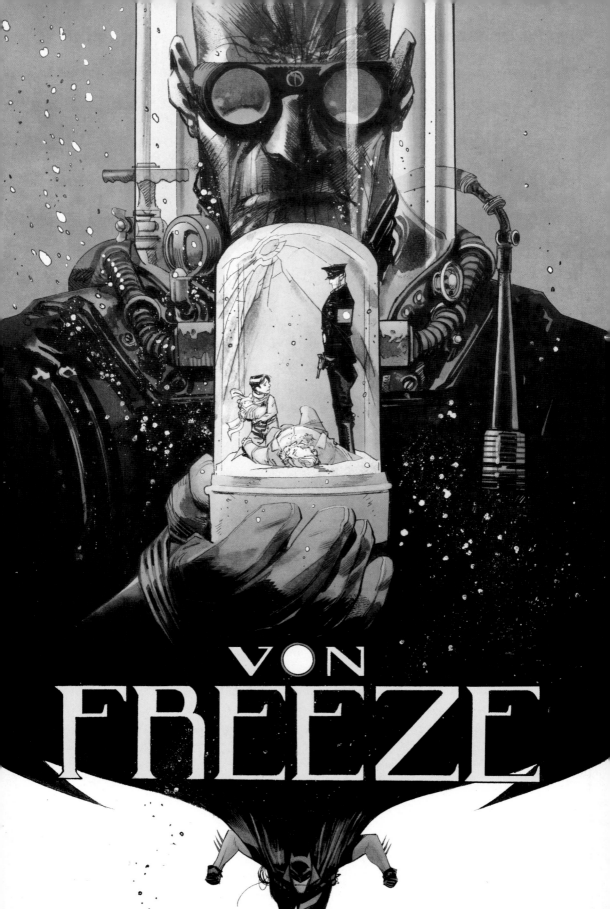

VON FREEZE

I wasn't able to hide the swell of emotion. As much as I tried to stop the tears, I couldn't. And sitting across the table from me was Klaus Janson, holding my hand.

Klaus had been an art hero of mine for many years. My style of inking is directly evolved from the work he's done over his long career in comics (most notably his work on *The Dark Knight Returns* with Frank Miller). When I first met him in New York City it was to teach a class of his at the School of Visual Arts. We went out to lunch after, had great chemistry and very similar senses of humor, and the next thing I knew I'd become close friends with one of my idols.

We shared many bottles of wine over the years, and talked about everything from intimate family troubles to how Klaus's family fled Germany during World War II. It was actually these two topics that brought us together for the book you're currently holding.

When I had my breakdown that day, it was because I hadn't spoken to my parents for over a year. And I wasn't able to digest how angry and hurt I was by them. Klaus had been through something similar, so it didn't take long for all the details to come pouring out. We were at that brunch to talk about a Mr. Freeze story; instead I ended up sobbing into my waffles at some overpriced hipster café.

After a few minutes I was able to collect myself, and Klaus hit me with it: "Maybe this is what our book should be about. It can be about broken families, and about the difficulty of moving on." And I immediately knew we had something.

I asked Klaus if he'd ever done a story with Nazis in it (most artists who are fans of Indiana Jones are dying to do at least one book with Nazi villains), and Klaus shocked me by saying he hadn't. And, of course, he'd love to. As the son of German immigrants, he said he had a lot of German guilt over WWII, and would really like to tackle the subject. Even if it would be emotional.

Which I'm guessing it was. There are a few panels where the story needed to show the ugly plight of the Jews—including a panel of them being experimented on with the Freeze tech. Drawing a panel for a day means living in an imaginary environment for a day, which isn't easy when it comes to the horrors of Nazi crimes.

But Klaus did it. He put everything into those panels, and it shows. I'm so proud of him.

I've rarely written for other artists, but I'm extremely happy with the results. This is the kind of book that almost never happens in comics—something put together by two people with a very close friendship, given permission by the publisher to basically do whatever they want, while diving into some very rough subject matter.

—Sean Murphy

P.S. I originally intended this story to be part of *Batman: White Knight*, but I ran out of space. So think of this one-shot as a deleted scene that falls between issues #6 and #7 of *Batman: Curse of the White Knight*—something secret about Mr. Freeze...

...TAKE THE BABY.

...NO MATTER WHAT HAPPENS... PROMISE TO LOOK AFTER HER...

I CAN'T ACCEPT YOUR OFFER. I CAN'T WORK HERE.

PLEASE--

NOT AFTER READING THOSE FILES YOU SENT ME, AND LEARNING WHERE THIS TECHNOLOGY COMES FROM.

I *REFUSE* TO BE A PART OF *WAYNE CRYOTECH.*

THERE'S MORE TO THE STORY THAN WHAT'S IN THE MILITARY RECORDS--

I DON'T CARE!

AND I DON'T CARE HOW MY FAMILY WAS INVOLVED--THIS WAS ONCE *FUNDED BY THE NAZIS*, AND I WON'T ACCEPT YOUR GUILT MONEY.

IT'S NOT GUILT MONEY--THE CRYOTECH BELONGS TO YOU AS MUCH AS IT BELONGS TO ME.

WHERE'S YOUR CONSCIENCE, VICTOR? I MEAN, HOW ARE YOU OKAY WITH THIS?

SOMETIMES I WALK INTO THIS PLACE AND FEEL A SENSE OF HOPE. ABOUT THE FUTURE OF MEDICINE AND THE LIVES WE CAN SAVE.

AND SOMETIMES I WANT TO BURN IT TO THE GROUND. TURN IT INTO A PILE OF SMOLDERING ASHES LIKE THE REST OF GERMANY, SO HISTORY CAN LOOK BACK AND FEEL LIKE HER SINS WERE CLEANSED.

HISTORY WILL NEVER FORGIVE EVIL MEN LIKE YOUR FATHER.

NOR SHOULD THEY.

LISTEN-- YOU HAVE GOOD REASON TO BE UPSET.

AND IF YOU WANT ME TO SHUT DOWN THIS LAB, *I WILL.*

BUT ONLY AFTER YOU'VE HEARD WHAT I HAVE TO SAY.

ABOUT HOW WE LIVED THROUGH THE WAR...

...AND THE *REAL REASON* WHY WE WERE FINALLY ABLE TO ESCAPE.

DOCTOR, COME QUICKLY--

MR. WAYNE IS HERE! HE NEEDS YOU--

BUT YOU HAVEN'T PRACTICED **FOR YEARS.**

YOU NEVER STOP BEING A SURGEON. BESIDES, YOU'LL BE THERE TO WALK ME THROUGH IT.

...

FINE.

...THEN WHY DON'T YOU INSERT THE IV.

IT'S A SIMPLE TASK--JUST FIND A VEIN...

...AND TRY TO KEEP A STEADY HAND.

...DAMN IT...

NO ONE RESPECTS YOU MORE THAN I DO, THOMAS. BUT THINGS ARE DIFFERENT NOW-- YOU'RE A--

A **BUSINESS-MAN,** I KNOW.

I WAS GOING TO SAY A **FATHER.**

IT'S DIFFERENT WHEN YOUR WIFE AND CHILD ARE ON THE TABLE.

I'M SORRY-- YOU'RE RIGHT.

YOU BUILT THIS FACILITY, HIRED THE BEST PEOPLE YOU COULD FIND. SO SIT BACK AND LET ME **DO MY JOB**--I CAN SAVE THEM.

I'M SORRY-- YOU'RE RIGHT.

NURSE, INJECT THE CRYO-GEL. BEGIN RUNNING THE FILTERS WHEN HER HEART RATE IS TWENTY BPM.

SHE'S GOING TO BE OKAY?

LET'S STEP OUTSIDE AND GIVE THE NURSES SOME SPACE. WE CAN MONITOR HER PROGRESS FROM THE OTHER ROOM.

I'LL MAKE SOME COFFEE. SEEMS LIKE WE HAVE A LONG NIGHT AHEAD OF US.

DON'T WORRY, THEY'RE BOTH IN GOOD HANDS.

BUT ALL I CAN THINK ABOUT IS MARTHA-- THE BABY DOESN'T EVEN SEEM REAL RIGHT NOW.

JESUS CHRIST, WHAT KIND OF HORRIBLE FATHER DOES THAT MAKE ME?

YOU'LL BE A GREAT FATHER.

YEAH?

AND YOU'LL BECOME WHAT-EVER YOUR FAMILY NEEDS YOU TO BE. BECAUSE YOU DON'T LIKE TO FAIL.

...THANKS, VICTOR.

SPEAKING OF SHITTY FATHERS, HOW'S YOURS? STILL IN TOUCH WITH THE BARON?

...

SORRY. I KNOW YOU DON'T LIKE TALKING ABOUT HIM. I'M JUST TRYING TO GET MY MIND OFF OF MARTHA.

WE DON'T SPEAK ANYMORE. IT WAS JUST TOO DIFFICULT.

WE PULLED HIM OUT OF GERMANY, CLEARED HIS CHARGES, AND BUILT HIM A LAB WITH EVERYTHING HE NEEDED--AND THAT ASSHOLE COULDN'T EVEN MUSTER UP A THANK-YOU.

GOD, I WOULD HAVE LOVED TO HAVE SEEN HIS FACE WHEN HE FOUND OUT YOU AND I WERE WORKING TOGETHER. WHAT DID YOU TELL HIM?

THAT YOU WERE OFFERING ME REDEMPTION. TO MAKE UP FOR ALL THE AWFUL THINGS HE DID DURING THE WAR.

AND FOR WHAT HAPPENED TO JACOB.

WHO'S JACOB?

JACOB SMITHSTEIN WAS BARON VON FRIES'S **BEST** FRIEND.

"THEY MET AT UNIVERSITY AND BONDED OVER THEIR INTEREST IN CRYOGENICS--AN UNEXPLORED FIELD AT THE TIME.

SMITHSTEIN & FRIES LABORATORY

"THE BARON WAS A SCIENTIST AND JACOB WAS A TRAINED DOCTOR WITH A FAMILY FORTUNE TO BACK THEIR BUSINESS. TOGETHER THEY HAD THE FOUNDATION TO CREATE SMITHSTEIN AND FRIES.

"THE ANTISEMITISM IN GERMANY ONLY MADE THEM **MORE DETERMINED** TO SUCCEED.

"THEY WANTED TO PROVE THAT GREAT THINGS COULD BE ACHIEVED IF GERMANY EMBRACED ITS DIVERSITY. THERE WERE SETBACKS, BUT BOTH MEN REFUSED TO QUIT.

"AFTER ALL, GERMANY WAS THEIR HOME, AND THEY WEREN'T GOING TO BE DETERRED BY A TEMPORARY SURGE OF RACISM."

"THEN CAME THE THIRD REICH.

"AFTER THE ELECTION, THE NATION HELD ITS BREATH, HOPING THE RHETORIC OF THE ANGRY MINORITY WASN'T TRUE...

"...HOPING THAT *NO MAN WAS THAT EVIL.*

"THAT'S WHEN THE BARON FIRST ASKED JACOB TO LEAVE. HIS FAMILY'S SAFETY WAS MORE IMPORTANT THAN THEIR WORK.

"BUT JACOB REFUSED-- IF THERE WAS GOING TO BE A WAR, THEN CRYOGENIC MEDICINE WAS GOING TO *SAVE LIVES.*

"JACOB INSISTED ON TRANSFERRING THE ENTIRE *SMITHSTEIN FORTUNE* TO THE BARON, SOMETHING MY FATHER WASN'T COMFORTABLE WITH. JACOB EVEN REMOVED 'SMITHSTEIN' FROM THE COMPANY NAME TO HELP PROTECT THEIR WORK.

"THEN HE MOVED HIS ENTIRE EXTENDED FAMILY INTO THE LAB, HOPING TO HIDE THEM UNTIL THE WAR WAS OVER."

"I WAS A YOUNG BOY AT THE TIME--JEALOUS THAT MY FATHER SPENT MORE TIME WORKING WITH JACOB THAN HE DID WITH ME.

"SO I USED TO SNEAK IN WITH MY TOYS AND TRY TO EMULATE HIM, HOPING THE BARON WOULD NOTICE.

"ONE DAY I ACCIDENTALLY KNOCKED OVER AN EXPERIMENT.

"MY FATHER WAS SO UPSET THAT HE *STRUCK ME.*

"I RAN AWAY SO HE WOULDN'T SEE ME CRY.

WHUD

"AND THAT'S WHEN JACOB FOUND ME.

"HE DIDN'T ASK WHAT HAPPENED--HE JUST PULLED OUT HIS MEDICAL BAG AND CLEANED THE WOUND."

"JACOB OFFERED ME SOMETHING MY FATHER NEVER DID--*LOVE*.

"I FINALLY FELT LIKE I HAD A FAMILY.

"IT WAS A DARK TIME FOR GERMANY, BUT THE SMITHSTEINS OFFERED ME WARMTH AND KINDNESS.

"EVERY NOW AND THEN SOMETHING WOULD HAPPEN THAT WOULD GIVE US HOPE AND REMIND US WHY WE NEEDED TO STAY BRAVE.

"LIKE THE DAY JACOB FOUND OUT HE WAS *GOING TO BE A FATHER.*

"JACOB'S WIFE ONCE TOLD ME A SECRET...

"...SHE DIDN'T THINK HER HUSBAND LIKED CHILDREN, BECAUSE HE WAS NEVER INTERESTED IN HAVING ANY OF HIS OWN.

"BUT SHE SAID THAT I HAD *CHANGED HIS MIND.*

"I WAS TOO YOUNG TO NOTICE MY FATHER'S RESENTMENT TOWARD JACOB.

"AND THAT'S WHEN THINGS REALLY SEEMED TO FALL APART."

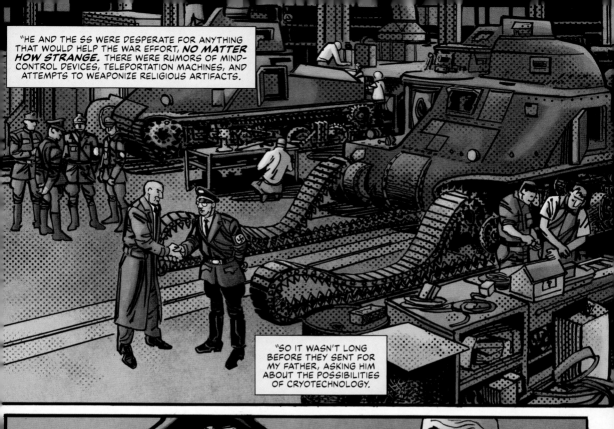

"HE AND THE SS WERE DESPERATE FOR ANYTHING THAT WOULD HELP THE WAR EFFORT, *NO MATTER HOW STRANGE.* THERE WERE RUMORS OF MIND-CONTROL DEVICES, TELEPORTATION MACHINES, AND ATTEMPTS TO WEAPONIZE RELIGIOUS ARTIFACTS.

"SO IT WASN'T LONG BEFORE THEY SENT FOR MY FATHER, ASKING HIM ABOUT THE POSSIBILITIES OF CRYOTECHNOLOGY.

"HIMMLER WASN'T INTERESTED IN MEDICINE--HE ASKED THE BARON ABOUT DEVELOPING A *DEATH RAY OF ICE.* HE PROMISED TO BUILD HIM A NEW FACILITY, AND TO FULLY FUND ALL HIS RESEARCH.

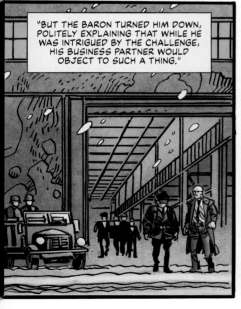

"BUT THE BARON TURNED HIM DOWN, POLITELY EXPLAINING THAT WHILE HE WAS INTRIGUED BY THE CHALLENGE, HIS BUSINESS PARTNER WOULD OBJECT TO SUCH A THING."

WHAT BUSINESS PARTNER?

"HIMMLER THEN REMINDED THE BARON THAT HE REALLY DIDN'T HAVE A *CHOICE* IN THE MATTER."

"AFTER THE MEETING, THE BARON DINED IN THE OFFICERS' CLUB--A PLACE FILLED WITH WEALTHY ELITES WHO SOUGHT OPPORTUNITY IN HITLER'S WAKE.

"THEY SUGGESTED IT WOULD BE BETTER FOR APPEARANCES IF MY FATHER *JOINED THE SS.*

"SO HE DID.

"JACOB FELL TO TEARS AT THE BETRAYAL. THE BARON NOT ONLY TURNED HIS BACK ON JACOB AND THE WORK THEY'D ACCOMPLISHED, HE ALSO TURNED HIS BACK ON AN *ENTIRE RACE OF PEOPLE.*

"BUT THE BARON DIDN'T FEEL HE HAD A CHOICE.

"HE HATED THE NAZIS, BUT HE FELT THAT WEARING THEIR UNIFORM WAS THE ONLY WAY HE COULD PROTECT THEIR WORK.

"BUT JACOB WOULDN'T HEAR IT--THIS HAD NOTHING TO DO WITH THE CRYOTECH. HE NO LONGER RECOGNIZED HIS FRIEND. WHATEVER THEIR HISTORY, WHATEVER THEIR DREAMS--IT WAS ALL OVER. AND HE REFUSED TO COOPERATE IN ANY WAY."

"MY FATHER EXPLAINED THAT IT WASN'T A WEAPON--IT WAS A MEDICAL TOOL. THE PATIENTS ALL HAD VARIETIES OF INJURIES AND ILLNESSES, AND THE BARON WAS JUST TRYING TO SEE HOW THE CRYOTECH COULD SAVE THEM."

MY PEOPLE ARE **NOT** YOUR LAB RATS!

THOCK

CRASH

STOP! I THINK I HEAR SOMETHING.

BARON VON FRIES--IS EVERYONE OKAY? I THOUGHT I HEARD SOMETHING.

IT'S OF NO CONCERN--JUST SOME EQUIPMENT THAT FELL OVER.

...

YOU NEED HELP PICKING IT UP?

NO THANK YOU-- PLEASE CONTINUE YOUR PATROL.

...

IS THERE A PROBLEM, SCHÜTZE?

...NO, SIR.

EVERYONE PUT ON YOUR WARMEST CLOTHING.

HONEY, FIND THE BAG OF SUPPLIES I'VE PLACED NEAR THE BED.

WE'RE LEAVING!

BUT JACOB--WE HAVE AN INFANT! AND MY MOTHER IS VERY SICK--

I REFUSE TO SUBJECT YOU TO ANOTHER MINUTE OF THIS *NIGHTMARE!*

THOSE SOLDIERS MIGHT BE COMING BACK--WE HAVE TO TAKE OUR CHANCES IN THE FOREST.

JACOB, *I'M BEGGING YOU TO STAY.* EVEN IF YOU MAKE IT PAST THE PATROLS, YOU'LL NEVER SURVIVE THE WEATHER! THINK ABOUT YOUR FAMILY--

YOU KNOW NOTHING ABOUT *FAMILY*, OR BEING A *FATHER!*

BECAUSE IF YOU DID THEN YOU'D *KNOW* WHY I'M LEAVING.

PLEASE DON'T!

VICTOR, LISTEN CAREFULLY.

MEET US DOWNSTAIRS BY THE BACK DOOR. *DON'T LET YOUR FATHER SEE YOU...*

RUN!

HALT!

OH NO...

÷GASP÷

CHECK FOR TRACKS IN THE SURROUNDING AREA-- THERE MIGHT BE MORE OF THEM.

I THOUGHT THEY WERE CRAZY WHEN THEY TOLD ME THERE WERE STILL JEWS IN THE AREA.

PLEASE-- I HAVE AN INFANT WITH ME.

I HEARD THAT JEWS HATED THE COLD... ...BECAUSE IT MAKES THEIR PENNIES TO STICK TOGETHER!

HAHAH

FHOCK

YOU KNOW THESE *JUDENSCHWEIN?*

OF COURSE I KNOW THEM. THEY ESCAPED MY FACILITY.

SO YOU ADMIT YOU WERE HIDING THEM?

THEY'RE PRISONERS-- IMPORTANT FOR MY EXPERIMENTS.

WHAT DO YOU MEAN... EXPERIMENTS?

SORRY, SCHÜTZE. IT'S ABOVE YOUR PAY GRADE.

IS IT?

IT'S BETWEEN ME AND THE FÜHRER. AND YOU FORGET YOU'RE *ADDRESSING A RANKING OFFICER--*NOW ROUND THEM UP AND TAKE THEM BACK TO MY LAB.

UNHARMED! OR I'LL REPORT YOU TO YOUR COMMANDER.

... PUT THE JEWS IN THE TRUCK. TAKE THEM DOWN THE MOUNTAIN.

KROOOO

JACOB-- JACOB I'M SO SORRY. THIS IS ALL MY FAULT.

PLEASE STAY ALIVE. TALK TO ME, TELL ME WHAT TO DO. HOW DO I SAVE YOU--

GEH...
...GEHH...

...GET...

...GET THEM OUT OF GERMANY.

÷GAAAAASP...÷

MMMMMM!

IS EVERYONE OKAY?

OH MY GOD, VICTOR...

YES. YES, I THINK WE'RE OKAY.

BUT JACOB...

I'M SO SORRY--

WE HAVE TO MOVE QUICKLY--GET INTO THE TRUCK BEFORE MORE MEN ARRIVE.

WHY SHOULD WE TRUST *YOU?*

...

DON'T WORRY.

WE'RE GETTING OUT OF GERMANY.

I PROMISE.

"USING HIS CONNECTIONS, THE BARON MANAGED TO GET THE SMITHSTEINS ALL THE WAY TO FRANCE.

"THEY WERE EVENTUALLY PICKED UP BY LA RÉSISTANCE..."

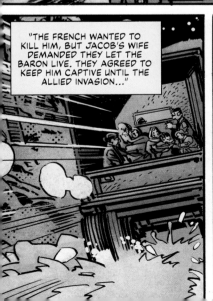

"THE FRENCH WANTED TO KILL HIM, BUT JACOB'S WIFE DEMANDED THEY LET THE BARON LIVE. THEY AGREED TO KEEP HIM CAPTIVE UNTIL THE ALLIED INVASION..."

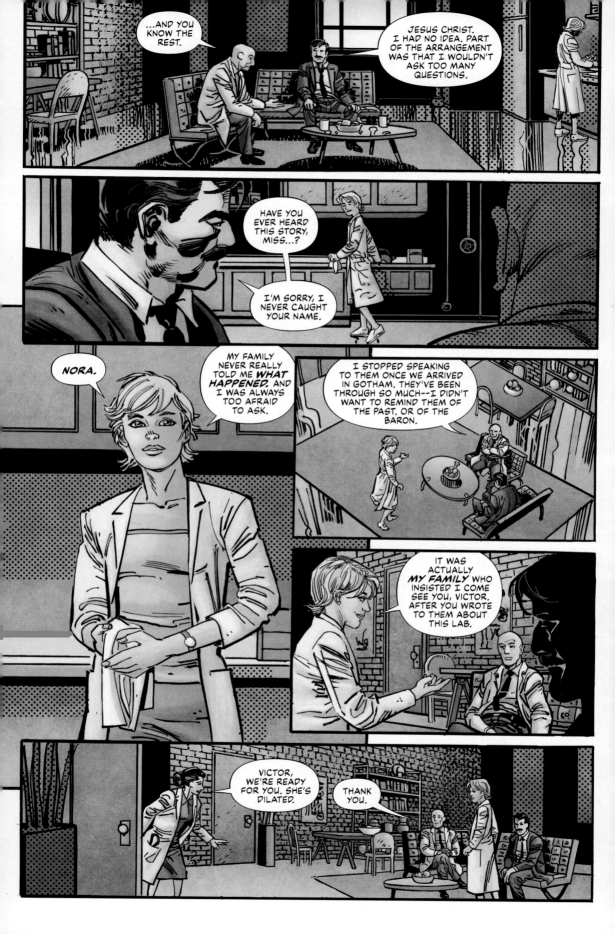

VICTOR, WAIT.

I WANT YOU TO HAVE THIS.

IT WAS MY GRANDFATHER'S.

I WAS GOING TO GIVE THIS TO MY SON ONE DAY, BUT I THINK YOU SHOULD HOLD ONTO IT FOR A WHILE.

BECAUSE... WELL...

...YOU KNOW.

THANK YOU, THOMAS.

THANK YOU, VICTOR.

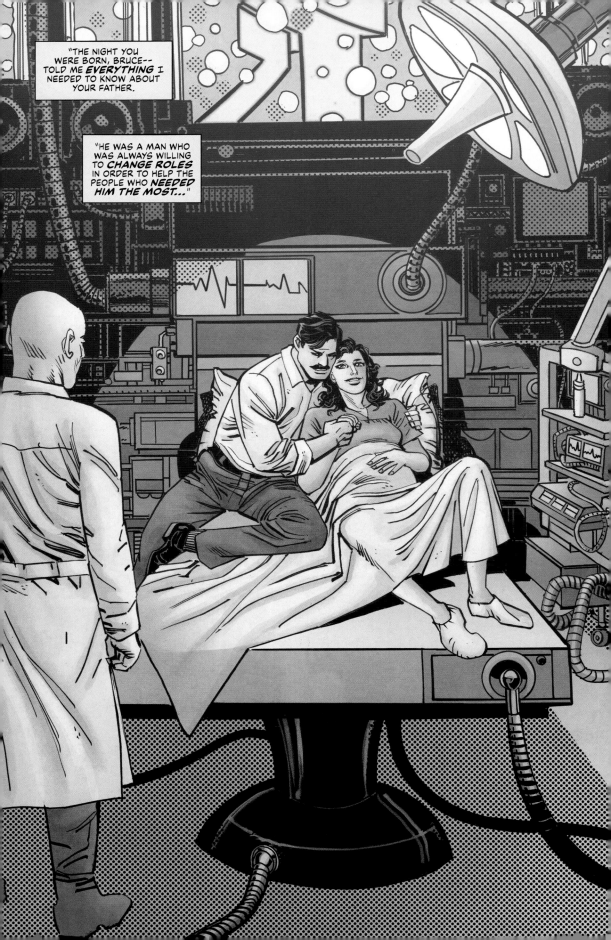

"THE NIGHT YOU WERE BORN, BRUCE-- TOLD ME *EVERYTHING* I NEEDED TO KNOW ABOUT YOUR FATHER.

"HE WAS A MAN WHO WAS ALWAYS WILLING TO *CHANGE ROLES* IN ORDER TO HELP THE PEOPLE WHO *NEEDED HIM THE MOST...*"

...WHETHER IT BE AS A HUSBAND, A SURGEON, A BUSINESS LEADER...

...OR A FRIEND...

...TO A TERRIFIED REFUGEE *LIKE* ME.

THAT *COMMITMENT TO OTHERS* RUNS DEEP IN YOUR BLOOD.

THAT'S WHAT MAKES YOU A *WAYNE.*

SO DON'T LET ANYONE TELL YOU OTHERWISE.

THANK YOU FOR THE WATCH, VICTOR.

I WISH I COULD BE MORE HELPFUL.

NO. YOU'VE GIVEN ME EXACTLY WHAT I NEED.

IF YOU NEED ANYTHING ELSE, YOU KNOW WHERE TO FIND ME.

GOOD NIGHT, BRUCE.

GOOD NIGHT, NORA.

GET WATCHA NEEDED?

BATMAN

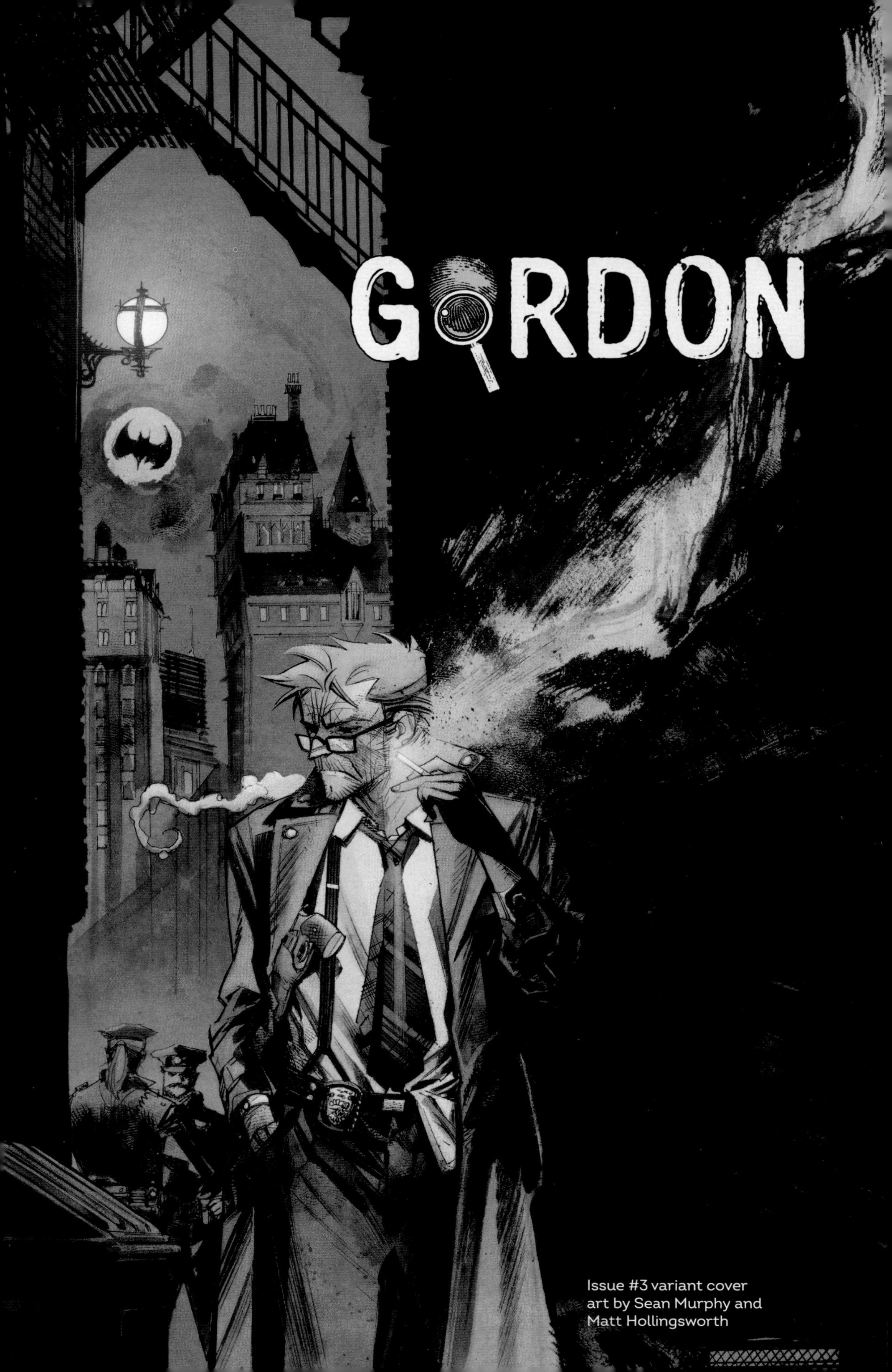

GORDON

Issue #3 variant cover
art by Sean Murphy and
Matt Hollingsworth

Issue #4 variant cover art by
Sean Murphy and Matt Hollingsworth

Issue #5 variant cover
art by Sean Murphy and
Matt Hollingsworth

BATGIRL

Edmond Wayne

Issue #6 variant cover
art by Sean Murphy and
Matt Hollingsworth

Issue #7 variant cover
art by Sean Murphy and
Matt Hollingsworth

Von Freeze variant cover art by Klaus Janson and Matt Hollingsworth

3A

4A

5A

6A

BATMAN with no mask holding Azrael's medallion. Harley and her hyenas in FG. Arkham in BG.

BATGIRL with guns. Smaller BATMAN on motorcycle driving off building

JOKER holding pistol, smaller BATMAN swimming under water. Boat on top. Flooded church on bottom left.

AZBAT with Azrael sword. BANE at bottom, holding broken BATMAN.

MAN BUN

BAKKAR

LEBONESE (BYZANTINE?) ≈1650

ST. DUMAS SYMBOLS →

BAKKAR IS A TEXTURE
MORE ABOUT SHAPE +
PATTERN THAN ANATOMY

BELT/SCARVES

BLUNDERBUSS PISTOL

BAGGY PANTS

ARABIAN SWORD

FLINTLOCK PISTOL

BATMAN: CURSE OF THE WHITE KNIGHT ISSUE 1   Sean Murphy 3-29-2019

BATMAN: CURSE OF THE WHITE KNIGHT COVER 2A   Sean Murphy 4-11-19

EDMOND WAYNE

ERROL FLYNN

BATMAN: CURSE OF THE WHITE KNIGHT COVER 3A   Sean Murphy 4.22.19

CAPE WINGS

BACKPACK
SWORD + GUN

GRENADES

CAPE "TATTERS"
DRAPE AROUND
WEAPONS PACK.

DE EAGLE

TATTERED CAPE
"WINGS" OF EAGLE

AZREAL

JEAN-PAUL JONES

BATMAN: CURSE OF THE WHITE KNIGHT COVER 4A   Sean Murphy 4.29.19

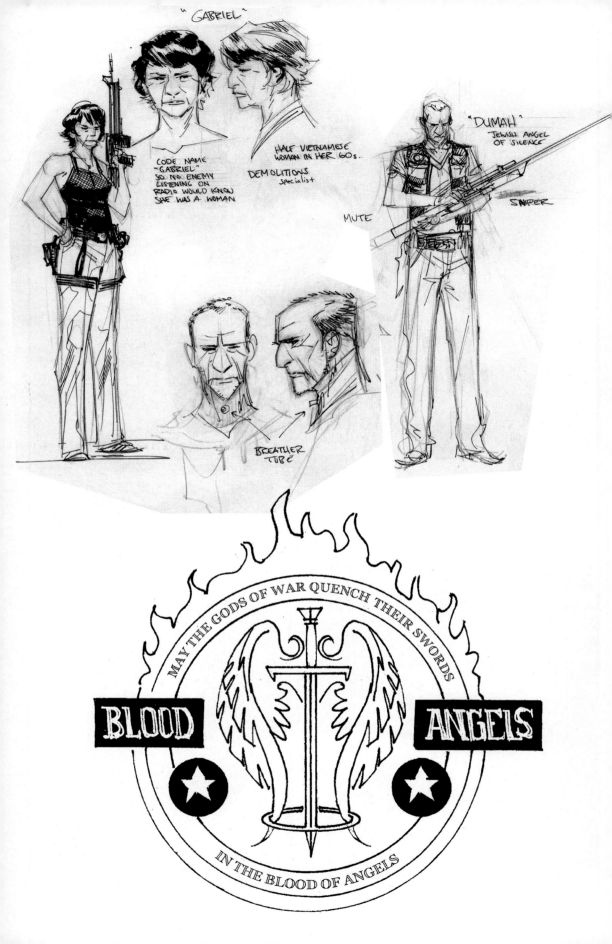

BATMAN: CURSE OF THE WHITE KNIGHT COVER 5A

BATMAN: CURSE OF THE WHITE KNIGHT COVER 6A   7.4.19

BATMAN: CURSE of the WHITE KNIGHT PAGE 7A   Sean Murphy 7-11-19

BATMAN: CURSE of the WHITE KNIGHT PAGE 8A   Sean Murphy 7-31-19

VON FREEZE COVER 1

After breaking into the industry at a young age, **Sean Murphy** made a name for himself in the world of indie comics before joining up with DC. Since then he has worked on such series as *Year One: Batman/Scarecrow*, *Teen Titans*, *Hellblazer*, *Joe the Barbarian*, and the critically acclaimed miniseries *American Vampire: Survival of the Fittest* and *The Wake* with Scott Snyder. Murphy also wrote and illustrated the original graphic novel *Off Road*, the popular miniseries *Punk Rock Jesus*, and the groundbreaking tales *Batman: White Knight* and *Batman: Curse of the White Knight*.

Klaus Janson was born in 1952 in Coburg, Germany, and came to America in 1957. As a child growing up in Connecticut, he learned how to read and write the English language almost exclusively from Lois Lane and Superman comics. An apprenticeship with mentor Dick Giordano encouraged Janson to continue with his passion, and after many summers of portfolio reviews and rejections, in 1973 Marvel Comics offered him a part-time office job applying gray tones to the black-and-white horror comic reprints that were then glutting the market.

In the 1980s Janson got his big break as an artist working with Frank Miller on the groundbreaking comic book series *Daredevil* and *Batman: The Dark Knight Returns*. Their success kicked off a long and celebrated career spent working on such titles as *The Amazing Spider-Man*, *The Mighty Thor*, *World War Hulk*, and *Wolverine*. Janson lives in New York City, where he writes, draws, inks, and colors comics, and teaches at the School of Visual Arts.

Born in Southern California in 1968, **Matt Hollingsworth** began his comics career in 1991. Since then he has worked as a color artist for most of the major American comic book publishers, contributing to such titles as *Preacher*, *Tom Strong*, *Catwoman*, *The Filth*, *Hellboy*, *Hawkeye*, *We Stand On Guard*, *Wytches*, *Alias*, *Daredevil*, and *Tokyo Ghost*. In 2004, while living in Los Angeles, he embarked on a two-year stint in the world of visual effects that led to assignments on seven feature films, including *Sky Captain and the World of Tomorrow*, *Serenity*, and his personal favorite, *Surf's Up*. In his free time he makes beer and is heavily involved in the beer scene in Croatia, where he lives with his wife and son.